# Francis Frith's
# AROUND NEWQUAY

PHOTOGRAPHIC MEMORIES

# Francis Frith's
# AROUND NEWQUAY

◆

Martin Dunning

FRITH
BOOK CO

First published in the United Kingdom in 2000 by
Frith Book Company Ltd

Hardback Edition 2000
ISBN 1-85937-140-x

Paperback Edition 2001
ISBN 1-85937-421-2

British Library Cataloguing in Publication Data

Francis Frith's Around Newquay
Martin Dunning

Frith Book Company Ltd
Frith's Barn, Teffont,
Salisbury, Wiltshire SP3 5QP
Tel: +44 (0) 1722 716 376
Email: info@frithbook.co.uk
www.frithbook.co.uk


Printed and bound in Great Britain

AS WITH ANY HISTORICAL DATABASE THE FRITH ARCHIVE IS CONSTANTLY BEING CORRECTED AND IMPROVED
AND THE PUBLISHERS WOULD WELCOME INFORMATION ON OMISSIONS OR INACCURACIES

# CONTENTS

# FRANCIS FRITH: *Victorian Pioneer*

**FRANCIS FRITH**, Victorian founder of the world-famous photographic archive, was a complex and multitudinous man. A devout Quaker and a highly successful Victorian businessman, he was both philosophic by nature and pioneering in outlook.

By 1855 Francis Frith had already established a wholesale grocery business in Liverpool, and sold it for the astonishing sum of £200,000, which is the equivalent today of over £15,000,000. Now a multi-millionaire, he was able to indulge his passion for travel. As a child he had pored over travel books written by early explorers, and his fancy and imagination had been stirred by family holidays to the sublime mountain regions of Wales and Scotland. 'What a land of spirit-stirring and enriching scenes and places!' he had written. He was to return to these scenes of grandeur in later years to 'recapture the thousands of vivid and tender memories', but with a different purpose. Now in his thirties, and captivated by the new science of photography, Frith set out on a series of pioneering journeys to the Nile regions that occupied him from 1856 until 1860.

## INTRIGUE AND ADVENTURE

He took with him on his travels a specially-designed wicker carriage that acted as both dark-room and sleeping chamber. These far-flung journeys were packed with intrigue and adventure. In his life story, written when he was sixty-three, Frith tells of being held captive by bandits, and of fighting 'an awful midnight battle to the very point of surrender with a deadly pack of hungry, wild dogs'. Sporting flowing Arab costume, Frith arrived at Akaba by camel seventy years before Lawrence, where he encountered 'desert princes and rival sheikhs, blazing with jewel-hilted swords'.

During these extraordinary adventures he was assiduously exploring the desert regions bordering the Nile and patiently recording the antiquities and peoples with his camera. He was the first photographer to venture beyond the sixth cataract. Africa was still the mysterious 'Dark Continent', and Stanley and Livingstone's historic meeting was a decade into the future. The conditions for picture taking confound belief. He laboured for hours in his wicker dark-room in the sweltering heat of the desert, while the volatile chemicals fizzed dangerously in their trays. Often he was forced to work in remote tombs and caves where conditions were cooler. Back in London he exhibited his photographs and was 'rapturously cheered' by members of the Royal Society. His reputation as a photographer was made overnight. An eminent modern historian has likened their impact on the population of the time to that on our own generation of the first photographs taken on the surface of the moon.

## VENTURE OF A LIFE-TIME

Characteristically, Frith quickly spotted the opportunity to create a new business as a specialist publisher of photographs. He lived in an era of immense and sometimes violent change. For the poor in the early part of Victoria's reign work was a drudge and the hours long, and people had precious little free time to enjoy themselves.

Most had no transport other than a cart or gig at their disposal, and had not travelled far beyond the boundaries of their own town or village. However, by the 1870s, the railways had threaded their way across the country, and Bank Holidays and half-day Saturdays had been made obligatory by Act of Parliament. All of a sudden the ordinary working man and his family were able to enjoy days out and see a little more of the world.

With characteristic business acumen, Francis Frith foresaw that these new tourists would enjoy having souvenirs to commemorate their days out. In 1860 he married Mary Ann Rosling and set out with the intention of photographing every city, town and village in Britain. For the next thirty years he travelled the country by train and by pony and trap, producing fine photographs of seaside resorts and beauty spots that were keenly bought by millions of Victorians. These prints were painstakingly pasted into family albums and pored over during the dark nights of winter, rekindling precious memories of summer excursions.

## THE RISE OF FRITH & CO

Frith's studio was soon supplying retail shops all over the country. To meet the demand he gathered about him a small team of photographers, and published the work of independent artist-photographers of the calibre of Roger Fenton and Francis Bedford. In order to gain some understanding of the scale of Frith's business one only has to look at the catalogue issued by Frith & Co in 1886: it runs to some 670

pages, listing not only many thousands of views of the British Isles but also many photographs of most European countries, and China, Japan, the USA and Canada – note the sample page shown above from the hand-written *Frith & Co* ledgers detailing pictures taken. By 1890 Frith had created the greatest specialist photographic publishing company in the world, with over 2,000 outlets – more than the combined number that Boots and WH Smith have today! The picture on the right shows the *Frith & Co* display board at Ingleton in the Yorkshire Dales. Beautifully constructed with mahogany frame and gilt inserts, it could display up to a dozen local scenes.

## POSTCARD BONANZA

◆

The ever-popular holiday postcard we know today took many years to develop. In 1870 the Post Office issued the first plain cards, with a pre-printed stamp on one face. In 1894 they allowed other publishers' cards to be sent through the mail with an attached adhesive halfpenny stamp. Demand grew rapidly, and in 1895 a new size of postcard was permitted called the

court card, but there was little room for illustration. In 1899, a year after Frith's death, a new card measuring 5.5 x 3.5 inches became the standard format, but it was not until 1902 that the divided back came into being, with address and message on one face and a full-size illustration on the other. *Frith & Co* were in the vanguard of postcard development, and Frith's sons Eustace and Cyril continued their father's monumental task, expanding the number of views offered to the public and recording more and more places in Britain, as the coasts and countryside were opened up to mass travel.

Francis Frith died in 1898 at his villa in Cannes, his great project still growing. The archive he created continued in business for another seventy years. By 1970 it contained over a third of a million pictures of 7,000 cities, towns and villages. The massive photographic record Frith has left to us stands as a living monument to a special and very remarkable man.

# Frith's Archive: *A Unique Legacy*

**FRANCIS FRITH'S** legacy to us today is of immense significance and value, for the magnificent archive of evocative photographs he created provides a unique record of change in 7,000 cities, towns and villages throughout Britain over a century and more. Frith and his fellow studio photographers revisited locations many times down the years to update their views, compiling for us an enthralling and colourful pageant of British life and character.

We tend to think of Frith's sepia views of Britain as nostalgic, for most of us use them to conjure up memories of places in our own lives with which we have family associations. It often makes us forget that to Francis Frith they were records of daily life as it was actually being lived in the cities, towns and villages of his day. The Victorian age was one of great and often bewildering change for ordinary people, and though the pictures evoke an impression of slower times, life was as busy and hectic as it is today.

We are fortunate that Frith was a photographer of the people, dedicated to recording the minutiae of everyday life. For it is this sheer wealth of visual data, the painstaking chronicle of changes in dress, transport, street layouts, buildings, housing, engineering and landscape that captivates us so much today. His remarkable images offer us a powerful link with the past and with the lives of our ancestors.

## TODAY'S TECHNOLOGY

Computers have now made it possible for Frith's many thousands of images to be accessed almost instantly. In the Frith archive today, each photograph is carefully 'digitised' then stored on a CD Rom. Frith archivists can locate a single photograph amongst thousands within seconds. Views can be catalogued and sorted under a variety of categories of place and content to the immediate benefit of researchers. Inexpensive reference prints can be created for them at the touch of a mouse button, and a wide range of books and other printed materials assembled and published for a wider, more general readership - in the next twelve months over a hundred Frith local history titles will be published! The

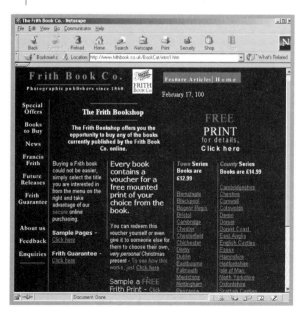

See Frith at www. frithbook.co.uk

day-to-day workings of the archive are very different from how they were in Francis Frith's time: imagine the herculean task of sorting through eleven tons of glass negatives as Frith had to do to locate a particular sequence of pictures! Yet the archive still prides itself on maintaining the same high standards of excellence laid down by Francis Frith, including the painstaking cataloguing and indexing of every view.

It is curious to reflect on how the internet now allows researchers in America and elsewhere greater instant access to the archive than Frith himself ever enjoyed. Many thousands of individual views can be called up on screen within seconds on one of the Frith internet sites, enabling people living continents away to revisit the streets of their ancestral home town, or view places in Britain where they have enjoyed holidays. Many overseas researchers welcome the chance to view special theme selections, such as transport, sports, costume and ancient monuments.

We are certain that Francis Frith would have heartily approved of these modern developments, for he himself was always working at the very limits of Victorian photographic technology.

## THE VALUE OF THE ARCHIVE TODAY

Because of the benefits brought by the computer, Frith's images are increasingly studied by social historians, by researchers into genealogy and ancestory, by architects, town planners, and by teachers and schoolchildren involved in local history projects. In addition, the archive offers every one of us a unique opportunity to examine the places where we and our families have lived and worked down the years. Immensely successful in Frith's own era, the archive is now, a century and more on, entering a new phase of popularity.

## THE PAST IN TUNE WITH THE FUTURE

Historians consider the Francis Frith Collection to be of prime national importance. It is the only archive of its kind remaining in private ownership and has been valued at a million pounds. However, this figure is now rapidly increasing as digital technology enables more and more people around the world to enjoy its benefits.

Francis Frith's archive is now housed in an historic timber barn in the beautiful village of Teffont in Wiltshire. Its founder would not recognize the archive office as it is today. In place of the many thousands of dusty boxes containing glass plate negatives and an all-pervading odour of photographic chemicals, there are now ranks of computer screens. He would be amazed to watch his images travelling round the world at unimaginable speeds through network and internet lines.

The archive's future is both bright and exciting. Francis Frith, with his unshakeable belief in making photographs available to the greatest number of people, would undoubtedly approve of what is being done today with his lifetime's work. His photographs, depicting our shared past, are now bringing pleasure and enlightenment to millions around the world a century and more after his death.

# Newquay – *An Introduction*

The north coast of Cornwall is a wild and beautiful place. Vast precipices of slate and sandstone, inhabited only by seabirds and the odd wheeling peregrine or raven, alternate with beaches of golden sand, and in the valleys and the lee of headlands lie communities sheltering from the Atlantic westerlies. The whole coast, from Bude in the north to Land's End in the far west, is at the mercy of these westerlies and the huge oceanic swells they bring with them. The only really sheltered anchorage is in the mouth of the Camel estuary, and to anchor here means having to negotiate the fearsome Doom Bar. Inland the country, though hilly, is rich and fertile, and there is a living to be made. Making a living from the sea on this inhospitable coastline is, however, another matter.

The Newquay area was first settled, as were many other Cornish communities, in the Bronze Age. A Bronze Age barrow or burial mound, perhaps 4,000 years old, can still be seen at Barrowfields just off Narrowcliff. In about 200BC the Iron Age came to Newquay in the shape of the cliff castle at Trevelgue Head; with it came the Celts, who were the ancestors of generations of Cornish men and women and whose language, though rarely spoken, still survives in Cornish place names. Indeed, Newquay's original name is in that very Celtic tongue: Tewynplustri, from the Cornish 'towan' for sandhill and 'lystry' for boats, translating as boat cove in the sandhills. Another version is Porth Lystry, meaning boat beach. Whatever the exact origin of the name, the implication is clear - with no sheltered anchorage, boats had to be beached to stay clear of the weather. The sheltered but narrow and shallow Gannel to the south and the little inlet of Porth to the north were the main ports in mediaeval times, but they were at the mercy of heavy weather.

A big step forward came in 1439, when Bishop Lacey of Exeter granted an indulgence for the building of 'a new keye for the rode of shipping'. The New Quay was built under the cliffs safe from the westerlies: the town has been known by that name ever since. Not that it was a town for many years; until the 19th century it was still essentially a fishing village, living on the great shoals of pilchards which were for many centuries the Cornishman's staple food. Huers at lookouts such as the Huer's Hut made a 'hue and cry' on huge brass horns when a shoal was sighted, and used a complex system of flag signals to direct the seine boats (of which there were up to 40 working from Newquay) in the tricky task of ringing the shoal. Catches of pilchards could be enormous; there is a recorded catch in one month of 8,000 hogsheads landed at Newquay, some 24 million fish. Lead and iron were brought from the mines inland, and coal and other cargoes landed on the beach at Porth and at Towan Beach, but the pilchard was king.

Things changed in the 1840s when the harbour was bought by the miner and magnate Joseph Thomas Treffry, also known as the 'King of Mid-Cornwall'. Treffry, whose mining interests lay nearer the south coast, was worried by shipping losses on the treacherous passage around Land's End. He enlarged the harbour and established a rail link via a tunnel in the cliffs direct to the harbour. Copper ores from his Fowey Great Consols mine crossed the peninsula on a tramway to Newquay, where they were either lowered down the steep incline of the tunnel in wagons or discharged down chutes ready for loading onto ships which would take them to the smelters in South Wales. China clay was also moved in this way; in 1872 Treffry built Island Pier, joined to the harbourside by a timber trestlework jetty, so that more ships could take on cargo.

In 1874 the old Trenance Viaduct, a precarious timber bridge to the south of the town, was replaced by a more substantial stone and iron girder structure, and the rail-

**TRENANCE VIADUCT 1907** 59338

way arrived in 1875. As with so many Cornish towns - Falmouth is one example, and Penzance another - the arrival of the iron horse was to change Newquay's fortunes forever - and not a moment too soon, for in 1870 the pilchard stocks had collapsed and life was the hotels were sprouting like mushrooms. The first of the big hotels was the Great Western on Cliff Road, and in 1898 the construction of the imposing Headland Hotel was begun at a magnificent site on Towan Head. Truro architect and businessman Sylvanus

NARROWCLIFF 1928 81262

hard.

In Victorian Britain, seaside holidays were becoming popular. The middle classes had more money and perhaps one week's holiday a year, and for the first time there was access to mass transport in the form of the railways. The journey to London, which previously might have taken up to a week, could now be accomplished in a day, and local entrepreneurs were quick to spot the opportunity.

In 1851 there were but two hostelries in the little village - the Red Lion (then known as Prout's Hotel) and the Old Inn - but by 1901

Trevail was responsible for the design, and the grandeur of the building reflects his style - pavilion roofs, Italianate masks in terra cotta, an Imperial staircase with a cast iron balustrade and Ionic columns in Devon Marble - all a far cry from the functional stone buildings around the harbour. What had been essentially a fishing village and harbour was becoming a major resort: by 1901 the population numbered over 3,000. Narrowcliff was developed as a residential area with fine private villas, but the hoteliers were not slow to recognise the potential of the fine views from the clifftop, and the villas quickly became hotels. A cinema was built, and theatres such as the Big Six and the Cosy Nook appeared. Visitors came not only to stay for a week or two, but also on day trips on bank holidays and for occasions such as Lifeboat Day.

Newquay became a favourite with the Royal family - King George V stayed in the Royal Suite at the Headland, and in the twenties and thirties the young princes, two of whom were later to become King, were guests at the Chief Constable's house above the harbour. Prince Edward was a particularly frequent visitor, and often played golf on the town course.

World War Two brought a new set of visitors in the shape of servicemen. Some came to stay at the Headland, but not to admire the view, for the hotel had become an amputation hospital. The Watergate Bay Hotel was requisitioned as an Officers' Mess by the RAF to house personnel from the airfield at St Mawgan; from here Avro Ansons patrolled far out into the Atlantic in search of U-Boats. St Mawgan was also first landfall for the Flying Fortresses of the United States Air Force, and American airmen became a common sight in the town, bringing with them many luxuries that had not been seen for some time because of rationing.

After the war, Newquay picked up where it had left off and continued building hotels. By 1960 Narrowcliff was almost unrecognisable - most of the villas had been replaced by flat-fronted three- and four-storey structures designed to utilise space as efficiently as possible. Down in the little harbour, life continued to run with the rhythms of the seasons and the moods of the sea. Diesel had replaced sail, and the few sailing luggers left were used for pleasure rather than for earning a living, but the fishing fleet still thrived - thirty to forty boats laid their pots for lobster and crab which would end up on the table of a hotel dining room. Island Pier still stood, but the wooden tramway was demolished in the fifties; where clay wagons would once have stood, today crab pots are stacked. The pilot gigs remain, now used solely for racing, and the lifeboat sits in its boathouse, having moved to the harbour from the old station at Towan Head in 1935.

Today's lifeboat is a very different vessel from those of old, such as the 'Admiral Sir George Back' or the 'James Stevens V'. In place of oars and sails are powerful twin outboards, enabling the present boat to have completed a rescue and be back in the boathouse in less time than it took for its ancestors to be launched. But the great Atlantic swells remain, rolling relentlessly in, and by a strange quirk of fate these same swells, the ones that caused the harbour to be built in the lee of Towan Head, today help contribute to the prosperity of the town. As they hit the gradually shoaling beaches, such as Fistral and Watergate, the swells rear up into majestic lines of surf which act as a magnet for surfers.

The winter population of 20,000 reaches around 100,000 in summer, swelled by those who come to surf or just to sit around enjoying the beaches. Hotels, surf shops and night clubs flourish, and the seagulls are more likely these days to live on pasties than pilchards. The town is unrecognisable as the tiny fishing village it once was, but in one respect things have not changed so much - as it always has done, Newquay still makes its living from the sea.

**TOWER ROAD 1918** 68671

Tower Road takes its name from the Tower (not quite visible in this photograph) which was built in 1835 for a naval captain. Subsequent owners included the Molesworths, one of Cornwall's most famous families, and the prominent engineer Sir Richard Tangye. It is now the clubhouse of Newquay Golf Club.

**CRANTOCK STREET 1918** 68673

On the left is the Fire Station. The awning on the right is that of 'Little Jenk's', so called to distinguish it from 'Big Jenk's' in town. Today it is a Post Office.

**BANK STREET 1912**  64810A
The building just visible behind the lamppost at the far left is the Devon and Cornwall Bank, premises which are now occupied by Trueform. Hartnoll's was lit by gaslight until well into the fifties.

**BANK STREET 1931** 84396
The imposing building on
the right is the new United
Reformed Church built after
the old one burned down.
Boots has now moved, and
their premises are today
occupied by Foster's.

**THE VICTORIA HOTEL 1900** 45855
The Victoria Hotel on East Street was built at the end of the 19th century; it has a lift that runs from the hotel right down to the beach. The property to the right is now Bertie's Nightclub.

**CLIFF ROAD c1960** N28198
The Great Western Hotel, which lies above the beach of the same name, was one of the first large hotels in Newquay. In 1890 a bed here would set you back the enormous sum of 5s (25p).

**CLIFF TERRACE 1892**
This view looks west along Cliff Road. The railway station is out of sight on the left, and the open area was the station yard, once the site of a railway turntable. The road on the right, just beyond the low wall, leads down to Great Western Beach. The long terrace of houses is now shops.

**NARROWCLIFF 1899**
On the left is the Trenarren Hotel, and peeping out from behind it is the old Great Western Hotel building. The building on the headland on the other side of the bay is the Atlantic Hotel.

**CLIFF TERRACE 1892** 31172

**NARROWCLIFF 1899** 43169

**NARROWCLIFF 1918** 68672

The seats on the right look out over Tolcarne Beach. On the left, the fine houses with their characteristic dormers are still private villas - the hotel takeover has not yet begun.

**NARROWCLIFF 1925** 78885

This photograph was taken from the junction of Narrowcliff and Edgecumbe Avenue. Not only have the hotels taken over, but the motor car is beginning its ascendancy - note how nearly all the hotels are advertising garages. The Trenarren Hotel is today part of the Great Western Hotel, and the Runnymede is now called the Crigga Bay.

**NARROWCLIFF 1925**
Despite the inroads made by the car, the horse cart was still in use in the twenties. The pavements have the hard-wearing granite kerbstones so characteristic of Cornish towns.

◆

**THE TOLCARNE HOTEL 1925**
That's entertainment, twenties style: dancing tonight at 8.30pm to the London Band, with Leslie Edwards, Jack Hylton's late pianist. Guests included Jack Peterson and Cornishman Len Harvey, famous heavyweight boxers of their time: after spending thirteen rounds trying to knock each other senseless in the ring, they would retire to the Tolcarne to convalesce together.

**NARROWCLIFF 1925**  78884

**THE TOLCARNE HOTEL 1925**  78886

**LIFEBOAT DAY 1928** 81253
Here we see the 'Admiral Sir George Beck' being
towed along Narrowcliff by the same draught horses
that were used to pull the lifeboat up the steep slip on
Towan Head. In 1935 the owner of the horses lost his
contract with the Great Western Railway and had to
sell his horses, so the lifeboat moved to the harbour.

**NARROWCLIFF 1928** 81261

The open area above the cliffs on the left is Barrowfields, a public open space which has at its western end a barrow (or tumulus), a Bronze Age burial site. There were once 15 barrows on Barrowfields, but all save one were razed to make way for a garage. On the far left below the clifftop is the Big Six Theatre.

**NARROWCLIFF 1928** 81263

This photograph was taken on Lifeboat Day, a fund-raising event which saw thousands of trippers arrive at Newquay. People dressed in their Sunday best: apparently there were even ladies in fur coats - despite the fact that the event was held on August Bank Holiday Monday.

**NARROWCLIFF 1928** 81262
Not only had the car established itself by
this time, but the charabanc had
appeared. Hocking's charabancs, silver
with maroon wings, took trippers on
excursions to places such as Bedruthan
Steps, the Luxulyan Valley
and Roche Rock.

**NARROWCLIFF 1930** 83075
On Tolcarne Beach, at the extreme left of the picture, beach huts and cafés are springing up to cater for the ever-increasing numbers of visitors. The Penolver Hotel is today part of the Beresford.

**NARROWCLIFF 1930** 83074
The first of the major hotel extensions on Narrowcliff has taken place: the Tolcarne Hotel is now four storeys high, and almost unrecognisable, save for the two bay windows of the original frontage which have been preserved.

**NARROWCLIFF c1960** N28192

Narrowcliff now looks very different from how it did in the twenties. Many of the hotels have followed the Tolcarne's lead and erected imposing frontages. Only the Cliffdene, on the left, preserves the look of the original villas.

**EDGECUMBE AVENUE 1918** 68677

Edgecumbe Avenue is named after local landowner Robert Edgecumbe, and leads inland from Narrowcliff towards Trenance. The building on the right is now Trevanion Flats, and the middle part of the other side of the road is today occupied by the Elliot Garth Hotel.

**EDGECUMBE AVENUE 1907** 59339

**EDGECUMBE AVENUE 1907**
Is the man in the straw boater thinking of buying? The house has only recently been completed, for the sign in the garden bears the names of the tradesmen involved: George Clark, Builder; George Card, Architect; H Checwidden, Decorator and J Penberthy, Plumber.

◆

**TRENANCE GARDENS c1960**
Trenance Gardens and Lake were created in 1932 by unemployed men, who were given a hot meal and tobacco in payment. In the background is the current Trenance Viaduct, completed in 1938 and bringing the branch line from Par.

**TRENANCE GARDENS c1960** N28181

### THE HOSPITAL 1931

The hospital on St Thomas' Road was opened by the Duke of Kent on one of his frequent visits to Newquay. Today it occupies the same site, but it is much altered and vastly extended.

### TREWERRY MILL 1907

Trewerry Mill lies three miles inland on a tributary of the Gannel not far from Trerice Manor, and now serves cream teas.

THE HOSPITAL 1931  84401

TREWERRY MILL 1907  59351

**TRENANCE VIADUCT 1907** 59338
Trenance Viaduct was first constructed in 1849
to bring china clay to Newquay Harbour. It was
originally a precarious-looking structure known as the
'Trenance Spider'; the arrival of the railway meant
that it had to be replaced with this more robust
structure in 1874.

**LIFEBOAT DAY 1928** 81255
Crowds are awaiting the launching of the lifeboat on
Lifeboat Day. The old boathouse (built in 1899 and now
an artist's studio) can still be seen on Towan Head, along
with the slipway, which at 1 in 2.25 was the steepest in the
country. The anchored boat with the mizzen rigged is the
'Only Two', owned by Percy Ede.

**LAUNCHING THE LIFEBOAT 1928** 81254

The lifeboat being launched here on Lifeboat Day is the 'Admiral Sir George Back', which was stationed at Newquay from 1921-35. It had ten oars and sails, and was last launched in 1934. The boys visible at the sides of the boat would jump off after the launch and collect money from the crowds in their red RNLI hats.

**TOWAN HEAD 1892** 31170

The building on the headland is a fish cellar. The cove in the foreground is where the Newquay lifeboat, the 'James Steven V', was lost in 1917.

### THE HEADLAND HOTEL 1900

When the Headland Hotel was built, the Hotel company enclosed an area of common land where fishermen had traditionally laid out their nets to dry. The fishermen demonstrated 'riotously' and won the concession of having the headland leased to the town council in return for not disrupting the building of the hotel.

◆

### THE HEADLAND HOTEL AND FISTRAL BAY 1901

The imposing edifice of the Headland Hotel was completed in 1900. It was designed by the celebrated Cornish architect Sylvanus Trevail, who was also chairman of the hotel company. The windows above the conservatory are those of the Royal Suite. During World War Two the hotel was used as an amputating hospital.

THE HEADLAND HOTEL 1900  45860

THE HEADLAND HOTEL AND FISTRAL BAY 1901  47744

**THE ATLANTIC
AND HEADLAND HOTELS 1912** 64804
The Atlantic Hotel (left, on the
headland) was the first large hotel to be
built in Newquay. Built between 1890
and 1892, its architect was also Sylvanus
Trevail. The old Lifeboat House (right,
with three windows) was built back from
the shore so as not to spoil the view from
the Headland Hotel.

**THE BEACON 1894** 33525
This quaint little building was once used by H M Coastguard. It is now under the war memorial, which was unveiled by The Prince of Wales in 1921. In the background is the Atlantic Hotel.

**THE HUER'S HUT 1907** 59333
The endearingly ugly Huer's Hut, standing on King Edward Crescent, is a reminder of Newquay's great days as a fishing port. Its exact age is unknown, but it could date from as early as the 14th century; it was used as a lookout for fish shoals.

**THE HUER'S HUT 1914** 66673A

Open on the seaward side, and with no glazing in the windows, the Huer's Hut must have been a draughty place; it probably needed its enormous chimney merely to keep the watchers warm. It was one of several strategic points from which men with large flags directed the seine boats in the difficult process of ringing the pilchard shoals.

**THE HUER'S HUT 1960** N28285

The Huer's Hut was restored in 1835 by a man named Vivian who, appropriately, was paid in fish for his endeavours. Newquay Town Council took over the lease of the building for a peppercorn rent in 1906.

**FROM THE FISH CELLARS 1887** 20244
Over a hundred feet high, the rampart
of Towan Head shelters the harbour
from the brunt of the fierce westerlies
that sweep in from the Atlantic. On the
point (right) is Fly Fish Cellars; the long
low building in the centre is
Active Fish Cellars.

**THE HARBOUR 1894** 33521
The wooden trestle pier (known locally as the Jetty)
connects South Pier to Island Pier, which was built in
1872 to increase the capacity of the harbour. The
prominent house on the hill above the masts of the
schooner was the residence of the
Chief Constable of Cornwall.

**THE HARBOUR 1894** 33518

Hidden at the end of the pier (centre) is the entrance to the tunnel that comes through the cliffs to allow railway wagons to bring cargoes to ships in the harbour. The tunnel emerged where Somerfield now stands on Fore Street.

**THE HARBOUR 1894** 33522

This photograph was taken from Eli Clemen's boatyard. The squat building on the cliff (left) was a grain store: from it grain ran down chutes to be loaded into vessels moored by the cliff just by the white boat.

**FROM THE HARBOUR c1900**
At the end of South Pier are empty wagons, and alongside the ship full ones, probably awaiting high tide to make loading possible. At the top of the beach on the right are the old fish cellars, now far less busy since the collapse of the pilchard stocks around 1870.

**THE HARBOUR 1907**
Compare this picture with photograph No N28502 to see just how fast Newquay was growing - almost all the gaps in the skyline have been filled with houses and hotels. In 1850, Newquay was still a small fishing village, but by 1907 the population was approaching 4,000.

**FROM THE HARBOUR c1900** N28502

**THE HARBOUR 1907** 59327

**THE HARBOUR 1907** 59328
Moored at bottom right are two traditional luggers, possibly built at St Ives, and the mainstay of the fishing fleet. The 'Ethel' (far right), by comparison, was a pleasure craft.

**ENTRANCE TO THE HARBOUR 1921** 70854
Like many Cornish harbours, that at Newquay has a very narrow entrance to protect vessels in harbour during heavy weather. The round structure on the right used to have an oil-fired red light which indicated the port entrance to the harbour. Today the job is done by electricity.

**THE HARBOUR 1925** 78866
The trestle pier still stands, but the harbour appears almost lifeless when compared with the bustle of 1894. The white boat in the centre foreground is a fishing gig, built without a centre thwart to allow nets to be carried.

**THE RED LION HOTEL 1888** 21185
Overlooking the harbour from North Quay Hill, the Red Lion Hotel is one of the oldest in the town, built around 130 years ago. Originally called Prout's Hotel, it started life as a coaching inn.

THE HARBOUR 1930 83061

### THE HARBOUR 1930

This photograph demonstrates just how sheltered Newquay harbour is, tucked into the lee of Towan head. While the storm rages around the rocks and beaches of Newquay Bay opposite, the boats in the harbour bob gently. The white boat second from right is the 'Sunny South', which later became an exhibit at Exeter Maritime Museum.

### THE HARBOUR 1950

The last traces of industrial Cornwall have gone. The trestle pier was demolished in 1950, leaving Island Pier as an island, and all trace of the railway lines has vanished. The building with the white windows on the harbourside (left) is the mission and reading room, standing roughly where the lifeboat station is now.

THE HARBOUR 1950 N28173

**THE HARBOUR FROM THE SANDS 1952** N28203

The harbour is now a place of pleasure rather than commerce. Tourists (including one woman who may or may not have been to Mexico) enjoy the beach, and most of the boats are diesel powered. The boat moored at Island Pier belonged to Pip Staffieri, maker of the best ice creams in Cornwall.

**THE HARBOUR 1955** N28245

Drawn up on the beach at centre is a small fleet of pilot gigs, light and manoeuvrable six-oared boats about 30 feet long and just under five feet wide. They were used by ship-handling companies up to the 19th century to take pilots out to incoming boats.

**THE HARBOUR c1960** N28264

For the crews of the pilot gigs, speed was of the essence to ensure that their pilot was the one that got the pillage fee, and so there arose a great rivalry between crews: this led eventually to the sport of pilot gig racing.

### The Harbour c1960

Gigs travel from port to port to take part in regattas; 'Shah' comes from St Agnes and 'Golden Eagle' and 'Bonnet' from St Mary's in the Isles of Scilly, spiritual home of gig racing. 'Ternary' (Newquay) is one of the fastest gigs afloat, and it is on her lines that most modern gigs are built. The oldest gig is the 'Newquay', built in 1812 and still

◆

### The Harbour c1960

Changing modes of transport: a fine selection of classic cars is parked on South Pier where the railway tracks once ran. They include a Morris Minor van, a Ford Consul, an Austin A30 and a Humber Snipe. The little white building is the Harbourmaster's Office.

The Harbour c1960  N28265

The Harbour c1960  N28268

THE SANDS 1901  47733
In the year of Queen Victoria's death, Victorian values
obviously still applied: drawn up on the beach just
above the water are twenty or so bathing machines,
designed to preserve the dignity of women bathers
and not outrage public decency.

**TOWAN BEACH 1921** 70851

The long low roof on the left is Speculation Fish Cellar. In the centre is the domed roof of the Pavilion Cinema (opened by George Robey), and the long terrace just below the skyline on the right is the coastguard cottages.

**TOWAN BEACH LOOKING EAST 1921** 70848

The prominent church tower on the skyline is that of the Wesleyan Methodist church, built in 1904, which still stands on East Street. The architects originally planned for it to have a spire, but this was never built. The field above Towan Beach was still grazed by bullocks from Killacourt Farm.

**TOWAN BEACH 1933** 85999

It is a mere thirty years after photograph No 47733, and the beach scene is quite different. There are many more people, probably from all classes, and the bathing machines have been consigned to history. Some of the swimming costumes on display, while modest by today's standards, would have caused quite a stir in Victorian

**FEEDING THE GULLS c1960** N28208

Don't try this today! Herring gulls, one of our most adaptable species, are noisy, opportunistic scavengers with a taste for pasties and fish and chips - and tourist's fingers. It is interesting to speculate whether Alfred Hitchcock ever visited Newquay.

**THE SANDS AND THE ISLAND 1907** 59320

Before the building of the famous suspension bridge in 1900, the Island was known as Jago's Island and used for keeping chickens. There was a café on the summit before the house was built in 1910.

**THE ISLAND AND THE SUSPENSION BRIDGE c1960** N28165

The private house atop the Island has had various owners, including the Lodge family. Sir Oliver Joseph Lodge invented the spark plug; he numbered among his friends Sir Arthur Conan Doyle, who is said to have stayed several times on the Island.

**DANCING ON THE BEACH 1912** 64790A
Newquay Town Band wear white hats
and play exclusively brass instruments.
The black hats and clarinet (left)
indicate that this may well be the
German band, which visited regularly at
one time. The big hotel on the clifftop is
the Edgecumbe, which later
burned down.

**ON THE SANDS 1912** 64802
Here we see a beach party composed entirely of the
fairer sex - with the exception of the rather lost-
looking little boy standing between the two girls at the
back. Perhaps this was an outing from a girls' school
or a convent. In the background is the
Great Western Hotel

**LUSTY GLAZE BEACH c1960** N28237
This picture shows all the traditional paraphernalia of a day out on the beach: deck chairs, rubber rings, surf boards and chalets. Lusty Glaze is the last of Newquay's beaches before the little inlet of Porth.

**CRIGGA ROCKS 1925** 78882
The enduring appeal of the beach: change the costumes, and the scene could be today. In the background, the woman in the pale dress appears to be doing the one-footed dance familiar to all who have ever tried to change while simultaneously preserving modesty and avoiding the perils of sand in the underwear.

**PORTH 1925** 78901

Along with the Gannel, Porth was one of the original ports of Newquay, and between 1818 and 1880 was used for shipbuilding. The long low building in the centre is Steven's yard, used for storing coal and other cargoes landed on the beach.

**PORTH BRIDGE 1912** 64815

Porth Bridge joins Porth Island or Trevelgue Head to the mainland. The earliest bridge was over 2,000 years ago, when Trevelgue Head was an Iron Age fort similar to many of the cliff castles built on Cornish headlands. Beyond the bridge, just round the corner, was the 'Banqueting Hall', a vast sea-cave which was often used for functions. If music was called for, a piano would be carried through the gully past where the little boy is standing!

**THE WATERGATE HOTEL 1900** 45858
The Watergate Hotel was built around the turn of the century in the false hope that the new railway was coming to nearby St Columb Major. It was designed by John Ennor, who also designed Newquay's sewage system. Famous guests included Baron von Richtofen. It continued in use as a hotel until World War Two, when it was requisitioned for use as an officers' mess.

**WATERGATE BAY 1918** 68664
After World War Two, the hotel became married quarters; then it stood empty until 1967, when it was turned into holiday flats. Over the winter of 1970-71 it was converted back to a hotel by Mr and Mrs Ashworth.

**MAWGAN PORTH 1914**  66687

Mawgan Porth lies three miles north of Newquay at the mouth of the pretty Vale of Mawgan, which runs inland to St Columb Major. On the hills above the vale is RAF St Mawgan, home of the search and reconnaissance Nimrods which patrol far out into the Atlantic.

**CRANTOCK, FROM EAST PENTIRE 1887** 20285

Crantock lies to the south-east of Newquay, opposite Pentire and on the south side of the Gannel (seen, at low tide, in the foreground). To reach Crantock from Pentire is a matter of a few minutes by ferry or on foot at the lowest of tides; the same journey by car round the head of the estuary is nearly five miles.

**CRANTOCK, THE CHURCH 1899** 43795

Crantock takes its name from St Garantoc, an Irish missionary who in AD 460 founded an oratory on the site. The present church is 16th-century; in this picture it is midway through restoration, having been neglected and fallen into decay in the 19th century.

**CRANTOCK, THE VILLAGE 1912** 64819
George Metford Parsons, who was Vicar from 1894 to 1924, was the inspiration for the rebuilding of the church, which was completed in 1902. A final touch was the addition of a clock, missing in photograph No 43795.

**CRANTOCK, THE VILLAGE 1912** 64820

The thatched white building on the left is now a private house. It was once the Ship Inn, which closed down during the Temperance movement that swept Cornwall in the 1830s as a response to the excessive drinking brought about by the smuggling of brandy.

**CRANTOCK, THE POST OFFICE 1918** 68678

The Post Office is now also the village shop, and extends into the rooms hidden by the bush. The clump of trees at the junction in the background surround what is now Crantock Round Garden, originally built as a pound to enclose stray animals from nearby commons.

**CRANTOCK, THE VILLAGE 1935** 86710
The little building on the left is Crantock Memorial Hall, built after the First World War and now also commemorating the dead of World War Two. Today it is used for community events.

**CRANTOCK, BEACH ROAD c1960** C181008
The centre of Crantock today is little changed, save for the telegraph poles and metalled roads. The curious conical structure in the centre was once the village well.

**CRANTOCK, WEST PENTIRE 1936** 87614

On the right is Crantock Beach at the mouth of The Gannel; beyond is Pentire Point East, which has Bronze Age burial mounds, or tumuli. The rocky island in the centre is The Goose. The large building is the West Pentire Hotel.

**CRANTOCK, THE BAY AND WEST PENTIRE SANDS 1936** 87615

Hidden round the corner of the headland is Pentire Point West, now owned by the National Trust, and beyond that is the charming little cove of Porth Joke. The footsteps in the sand might be heading for Vugga Cove, hidden on the left and once the haunt of smugglers.

**CRANTOCK,**
*East Pentire and Towan Heads 1936*
Pentire Point East is the nearest
headland, and poking out from behind
it is Towan Head. The shadowy coastline
in the background runs north north
west for twelve miles to Trevose Head,
just visible on the left of the picture.

**FERN PIT ON THE GANNEL 1901**
On the left is a houseboat, long since
gone, and to its right the little quay was
the landing place for the ferry. Boats
could be hired here for an afternoon
messing about on the Gannel.

CRANTOCK, EAST PENTIRE AND TOWAN HEADS 1936  87617

FERN PIT ON THE GANNEL 1901  47747

**FERN PIT AND WEST PENTIRE 1904** 52303

Fern Pit, owned by successive generations of Northeys, was a popular tea room. In 1938 a huge quantity of pit props from a wreck was washed up on Crantock Beach. The locals put them to good use.

**PENTIRE, THE GANNEL c1955** P359006

In the 18th century Welsh coal was landed on the Gannel, at Penpol (hidden at centre right) and at Trevemper, at the head of the estuary in the far distance. Today the estuary is choked with sand and far too shallow for large

**CROSSING THE GANNEL 1925** 78898
In the field on the hill behind, stooks of corn from Trethelan Farm are stacked to dry. The hill is now built up, but the little bridge survives, negotiable only at low tide.

**THE RIVER GANNEL 1928** 81295

The River Gannel (Cornish for 'channel' or 'crooked estuary') rises inland near the chapel at Fraddon and flows ten miles to reach its estuary. Here at the Gannel Regatta the race in progress is for outboard motor boats, and is being led by Edward Jenkin in 'Maquarie'.

**THE GANNEL 1928** 81300

This pictures harks back to more prosperous time for The Gannel. In the mid 19th century it was an important boat building area, with sailing schooners being built on the foreshore. The schooner here is the 'Ada', which later became a museum on Penpol Creek.

### THE GANNEL 1928
Here we see the crossing from the south side of the Gannel to Newquay by ferry. Ferries such as this are common on Cornish estuaries, and are often summoned by shouting or whistling. Here Dick Northey, who owned Fern Pit, is bringing the ferry in on Crantock Beach.

### PENTIRE
#### *Fistral Bay c1955*
Facing west, directly into the Atlantic swells, and with a gently sloping beach, Fistral Bay has some of the best surf in the country; it is regularly the venue for competitions, including, on occasion, the World Championships. The large building on the other side of the bay is the Headland Hotel.

**THE GANNEL 1928** 81302

**PENTIRE, FISTRAL BAY c1955** P359009

**FISTRAL BAY c1960** N28286

**FISTRAL BAY c1960**
This photograph was taken from the north end of Fistral Beach, just where the road leads to the corner of the beach in photograph No P359009. Pentire Point East is the obvious headland, with The Goose just to the right. The large building on the skyline is the Pentire Hotel.

**PENTIRE 1918**
This view looks back inland to another age: there are still wide open spaces between the houses, the road is not made up, and there are no street lights or overhead cables.

**PENTIRE 1918** 68688

**PENTIRE 1918** 68646
On the far left skyline are the exposed houses of Atlantic Road. The house with the arched doorway just right of centre was built by R J Clemens and is now flats.

**PENTIRE, THE BAY HOTEL 1928** 81273
In the ten years after photograph No 68646 the area is considerably more built up; the house in the centre of the picture is now surrounded, and the Bay Hotel (also built by R J Clemens) has doubled in size.

**THE GOLF COURSE 1907** 59337
The long low building is the Clubhouse, and behind it
is the Tower. At one time, before Sunday golf, the golf
course was a popular spot for Sunday picnics.

**PENTIRE, THE COAST FROM THE GOLF LINKS c1955** P359003
Newquay Golf Links was laid out in the 1890s and enjoys a fine view over Fistral Bay and out towards Pentire Point East. Prince Edward (later Edward VIII and then Duke of Windsor) played golf here.

**THE GOLF LINKS 1925** 78891
This picture shows just why Fistral Beach is such a Mecca for surfers - long lines of clean, evenly breaking surf. But in 1925 there appears not to be a surfer in sight - the sport had not yet arrived from California.

### ATLANTIC ROAD 1918
The fine terrace of Atlantic Road runs parallel to Higher Tower Road and has magnificent views out over Fistral Beach. The downside is the wind - local lore has it that there were always one or two houses empty here because of the exposed position! At the far end of the road is the old cemetery.

### PENTIRE
*View from the Post Office c1955*
How quiet the street seems! No road markings, no double yellow lines and no cars. The grassy patch beyond the telephone box was the national Children's Home playground, and the hotel on the far right was the St Rumon, now the esplanade.

ATLANTIC ROAD 1918   68676

PENTIRE, VIEW FROM THE POST OFFICE C1955   P359004

**THE FISTRAL BAY HOTEL 1931** 84399

The Fistral Bay Hotel was built at around the turn of the century. The bus going down the hill belongs to Western National - the same company that runs the bus service today.

**PENTIRE, THE FISTRAL BAY HOTEL c1955** P359010

Here we see another view of the Fistral Bay Hotel, but now with three storeys rather than two. The extra storey was added sometime before World War Two.

# Index

# Frith Book Co Titles

Town Books 96pp, 100 photos. County and Themed Books 128pp, 150 photos
(unless specified) All titles hardback laminated case and jacket
except those indicated pb (paperback)

| | | |
|---|---|---|
| Around Barnstaple | 1-85937-084-5 | £12.99 |
| Around Blackpool | 1-85937-049-7 | £12.99 |
| Around Bognor Regis | 1-85937-055-1 | £12.99 |
| Around Bristol | 1-85937-050-0 | £12.99 |
| Around Cambridge | 1-85937-092-6 | £12.99 |
| Cheshire | 1-85937-045-4 | £14.99 |
| Around Chester | 1-85937-090-X | £12.99 |
| Around Chesterfield | 1-85937-071-3 | £12.99 |
| Around Chichester | 1-85937-089-6 | £12.99 |
| Cornwall | 1-85937-054-3 | £14.99 |
| Cotswolds | 1-85937-099-3 | £14.99 |
| Around Derby | 1-85937-046-2 | £12.99 |
| Devon | 1-85937-052-7 | £14.99 |
| Dorset | 1-85937-075-6 | £14.99 |
| Dorset Coast | 1-85937-062-4 | £14.99 |
| Around Dublin | 1-85937-058-6 | £12.99 |
| East Anglia | 1-85937-059-4 | £14.99 |
| Around Eastbourne | 1-85937-061-6 | £12.99 |
| English Castles | 1-85937-078-0 | £14.99 |
| Around Falmouth | 1-85937-066-7 | £12.99 |
| Hampshire | 1-85937-064-0 | £14.99 |
| Isle of Man | 1-85937-065-9 | £14.99 |
| Around Maidstone | 1-85937-056-X | £12.99 |
| North Yorkshire | 1-85937-048-9 | £14.99 |
| Around Nottingham | 1-85937-060-8 | £12.99 |
| Around Penzance | 1-85937-069-1 | £12.99 |
| Around Reading | 1-85937-087-X | £12.99 |
| Around St Ives | 1-85937-068-3 | £12.99 |
| Around Salisbury | 1-85937-091-8 | £12.99 |
| Around Scarborough | 1-85937-104-3 | £12.99 |
| Scottish Castles | 1-85937-077-2 | £14.99 |
| Around Sevenoaks and Tonbridge | 1-85937-057-8 | £12.99 |

| | | |
|---|---|---|
| Sheffield and S Yorkshire | 1-85937-070-5 | £14.99 |
| Shropshire | 1-85937-083-7 | £14.99 |
| Staffordshire | 1-85937-047-0 (96pp) | £12.99 |
| Suffolk | 1-85937-074-8 | £14.99 |
| Surrey | 1-85937-081-0 | £14.99 |
| Around Torbay | 1-85937-063-2 | £12.99 |
| Wiltshire | 1-85937-053-5 | £14.99 |
| Around Bakewell | 1-85937-113-2 | £12.99 |
| Around Bournemouth | 1-85937-067-5 | £12.99 |
| Cambridgeshire | 1-85937-086-1 | £14.99 |
| Essex | 1-85937-082-9 | £14.99 |
| Around Great Yarmouth | 1-85937-085-3 | £12.99 |
| Hertfordshire | 1-85937-079-9 | £14.99 |
| Isle of Wight | 1-85937-114-0 | £14.99 |
| Around Lincoln | 1-85937-111-6 | £12.99 |
| Oxfordshire | 1-85937-076-4 | £14.99 |
| Around Shrewsbury | 1-85937-110-8 | £12.99 |
| South Devon Coast | 1-85937-107-8 | £14.99 |
| Around Stratford upon Avon | 1-85937-098-5 | £12.99 |
| West Midlands | 1-85937-109-4 | £14.99 |

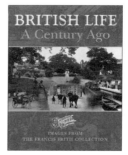

British Life A Century Ago
246 x 189mm
144pp, hardback.
Black and white
Lavishly illustrated with photos
from the turn of the century,
and with extensive commentary.
It offers a unique insight into
the social history and heritage
of bygone Britain.

1-85937-103-5 £17.99

# Available from your local bookshop or from the publisher

# Frith Book Co Titles Available in 2000

| | | | | |
|---|---|---|---|---|
| Around Bath | 1-85937-097-7 | £12.99 | Mar | |
| County Durham | 1-85937-123-x | £14.99 | Mar | |
| Cumbria | 1-85937-101-9 | £14.99 | Mar | |
| Down the Thames | 1-85937-121-3 | £14.99 | Mar | |
| Around Exeter | 1-85937-126-4 | £12.99 | Mar | |
| Greater Manchester | 1-85937-108-6 | £14.99 | Mar | |
| Around Guildford | 1-85937-117-5 | £12.99 | Mar | |
| Around Harrogate | 1-85937-112-4 | £12.99 | Mar | |
| Around Leicester | 1-85937-073-x | £12.99 | Mar | |
| Around Liverpool | 1-85937-051-9 | £12.99 | Mar | |
| Around Newark | 1-85937-105-1 | £12.99 | Mar | |
| Northumberland and Tyne & Wear | | | | |
| | 1-85937-072-1 | £14.99 | Mar | |
| Around Oxford | 1-85937-096-9 | £12.99 | Mar | |
| Around Plymouth | 1-85937-119-1 | £12.99 | Mar | |
| Around Southport | 1-85937-106-x | £12.99 | Mar | |
| Welsh Castles | 1-85937-120-5 | £14.99 | Mar | |
| | | | | |
| Around Belfast | 1-85937-094-2 | £12.99 | Apr | |
| Canals and Waterways | 1-85937-129-9 | £17.99 | Apr | |
| Down the Severn | 1-85937-118-3 | £14.99 | Apr | |
| East Sussex | 1-85937-130-2 | £14.99 | Apr | |
| Exmoor | 1-85937-132-9 | £14.99 | Apr | |
| Gloucestershire | 1-85937-102-7 | £14.99 | Apr | |
| Around Horsham | 1-85937-127-2 | £12.99 | Apr | |
| Around Ipswich | 1-85937-133-7 | £12.99 | Apr | |
| Ireland (pb) | 1-85937-181-7 | £9.99 | Apr | |
| Kent Living Memories | 1-85937-125-6 | £14.99 | Apr | |
| London (pb) | 1-85937-183-3 | £9.99 | Apr | |
| New Forest | 1-85937-128-0 | £14.99 | Apr | |
| Scotland (pb) | 1-85937-182-5 | £9.99 | Apr | |
| Around Southampton | 1-85937-088-8 | £12.99 | Apr | |
| Stone Circles & Ancient Monuments | | | | |
| | 1-85937-143-4 | £17.99 | Apr | |
| Sussex (pb) | 1-85937-184-1 | £9.99 | Apr | |
| | | | | |
| Colchester (pb) | 1-85937-188-4 | £8.99 | May | |
| County Maps of Britain | | | | |
| | 1-85937-156-6 | (192pp) £19.99 | May | |
| Leicestershire (pb) | 1-85937-185-x | £9.99 | May | |
| Lincolnshire | 1-85937-135-3 | £14.99 | May | |
| Around Newquay | 1-85937-140-x | £12.99 | May | |
| Nottinghamshire (pb) | 1-85937-187-6 | £9.99 | May | |
| Redhill to Reigate | 1-85937-137-x | £12.99 | May | |
| Victorian & Edwardian Yorkshire | | | | |
| | 1-85937-154-x | £14.99 | May | |
| Around Winchester | 1-85937-139-6 | £12.99 | May | |
| Yorkshire (pb) | 1-85937-186-8 | £9.99 | May | |
| | | | | |
| Berkshire (pb) | 1-85937-191-4 | £9.99 | Jun | |
| Brighton (pb) | 1-85937-192-2 | £8.99 | Jun | |
| Dartmoor | 1-85937-145-0 | £14.99 | Jun | |
| East London | 1-85937-080-2 | £14.99 | Jun | |
| Glasgow (pb) | 1-85937-190-6 | £8.99 | Jun | |
| Kent (pb) | 1-85937-189-2 | £9.99 | Jun | |
| Victorian & Edwardian Kent | | | | |
| | 1-85937-149-3 | £14.99 | Jun | |
| North Devon Coast | 1-85937-146-9 | £14.99 | Jun | |
| Peak District | 1-85937-100-0 | £14.99 | Jun | |
| Around Truro | 1-85937-147-7 | £12.99 | Jun | |
| Victorian & Edwardian Maritime Album | | | | |
| | 1-85937-144-2 | £17.99 | Jun | |
| West Sussex | 1-85937-148-5 | £14.99 | Jun | |
| | | | | |
| Churches of Berkshire | 1-85937-170-1 | £17.99 | Jul | |
| Churches of Dorset | 1-85937-172-8 | £17.99 | Jul | |
| Churches of Hampshire | 1-85937-207-4 | £17.99 | Jul | |
| Churches of Wiltshire | 1-85937-171-x | £17.99 | Jul | |
| Derbyshire (pb) | 1-85937-196-5 | £9.99 | Jul | |
| Edinburgh (pb) | 1-85937-193-0 | £8.99 | Jul | |
| Herefordshire | 1-85937-174-4 | £14.99 | Jul | |
| Norwich (pb) | 1-85937-194-9 | £8.99 | Jul | |
| Ports and Harbours | 1-85937-208-2 | £17.99 | Jul | |
| Somerset and Avon | 1-85937-153-1 | £14.99 | Jul | |
| South Devon Living Memories | | | | |
| | 1-85937-168-x | £14.99 | Jul | |
| Warwickshire (pb) | 1-85937-203-1 | £9.99 | Jul | |
| Worcestershire | 1-85937-152-3 | £14.99 | Jul | |
| Yorkshire Living Memories | | | | |
| | 1-85937-166-3 | £14.99 | Jul | |

# FRITH PRODUCTS & SERVICES

Francis Frith would doubtless be pleased to know that the pioneering publishing venture he started in 1860 still continues today. More than a hundred and thirty years later, The Francis Frith Collection continues in the same innovative tradition and is now one of the foremost publishers of vintage photographs in the world. Some of the current activities include:

## Interior Decoration

Today Frith's photographs can be seen framed and as giant wall murals in thousands of pubs, restaurants, hotels, banks, retail stores and other public buildings throughout the country. In every case they enhance the unique local atmosphere of the places they depict and provide reminders of gentler days in an increasingly busy and frenetic world.

## Product Promotions

Frith products have been used by many major companies to promote the sales of their own products or to reinforce their own history and heritage. Brands include Hovis bread, Courage beers, Scots Porage Oats, Colman's mustard, Cadbury's foods, Mellow Birds coffee, Dunhill pipe tobacco, Guinness, and Bulmer's Cider.

## Genealogy and Family History

As the interest in family history and roots grows world-wide, more and more people are turning to Frith's photographs of Great Britain for images of the towns, villages and streets where their ancestors lived; and, of course, photographs of the churches and chapels where their ancestors were christened, married and buried are an essential part of every genealogy tree and family album.

A series of easy-to-use CD Roms is planned for publication, and an increasing number of Frith photographs will be able to be viewed on specialist genealogy sites. A growing range of Frith books will be available on CD.

## The Internet

Already thousands of Frith photographs can be viewed and purchased on the internet. By the end of the year 2000 some 60,000 Frith photographs will be available on the internet. The number of sites is constantly expanding, each focussing on different products and services from the Collection.
Some of the sites are listed below.

www.townpages.co.uk
www.icollector.com
www.barclaysquare.co.uk
www.cornwall-online.co.uk

For background information on the Collection look at the three following sites:

www.francisfrith.com
www.francisfrith.co.uk
www.frithbook.co.uk

## Frith Products

All Frith photographs are available Framed or just as Mounted Prints, and can be ordered from the address below. From time to time other products - Address Books, Calendars, Table Mats, etc - are available.

> **For further information:**
> if you would like further information on any of the above aspects of the Frith business please contact us at the address below:
> **The Francis Frith Collection,**
> **Frith's Barn, Teffont, Salisbury, Wiltshire,**
> **England SP3 5QP.**
> Tel: +44 (0)1722 716 376  Fax: +44 (0)1722 716 881   Email: uksales@francisfrith.com

# To receive your FREE Mounted Print

**Mounted Print**
*Overall size 14 x 11 inches*

*Cut out this Voucher and return it with your remittance for £1.50 to cover postage and handling. Choose any photograph included in this book. Your SEPIA print will be A4 in size, and mounted in a cream mount with burgundy rule lines, overall size 14 x 11 inches.*

## Order additional Mounted Prints at HALF PRICE (only £7.49 each*)

If there are further pictures you would like to order, possibly as gifts for friends and family, acquire them at half price (no additional postage and handling required).

## Have your Mounted Prints framed*

For an additional £14.95 per print you can have your chosen Mounted Print framed in an elegant polished wood and gilt moulding, overall size 16 x 13 inches (no additional postage and handling required).

> **\* IMPORTANT!**
> These special prices are only available if ordered using the original voucher on this page (no copies permitted) and at the same time as your free Mounted Print, for delivery to the same address

## Frith Collectors' Guild

*From time to time we publish a magazine of news and stories about Frith photographs and further special offers of Frith products. If you would like 12 months FREE membership, please return this form.*

*Send completed forms to:*

**The Francis Frith Collection, Frith's Barn, Teffont, Salisbury, Wiltshire SP3 5QP**

## Voucher for FREE and Reduced Price Frith Prints

| Picture no. | Page number | Qty | Mounted @ £7.49 | Framed + £14.95 | Total Cost |
|---|---|---|---|---|---|
| | | 1 | Free of charge* | £ | £ |
| | | | £7.49 | £ | £ |
| | | | £7.49 | £ | £ |
| | | | £7.49 | £ | £ |
| | | | £7.49 | £ | £ |
| | | | £7.49 | £ | £ |

| | |
|---|---|
| * Post & handling | £1.50 |

**Book Title** . . . . . . . . . . . . . . .   **Total Order Cost** | £

*Please do not photocopy this voucher. Only the original is valid, so please cut it out and return it to us.*

I enclose a cheque / postal order for £ . . . . . . . . . . .
made payable to 'The Francis Frith Collection'
OR please debit my Mastercard / Visa / Switch / Amex card

Number . . . . . . . . . . . . . . . . . . . . . . . . . . . . . . . . . . .

Expires . . . . . . . . . .   Signature . . . . . . . . . . . . . . . . . . . . . . .

Name  Mr/Mrs/Ms . . . . . . . . . . . . . . . . . . . . . . . . . . . . . . . . . .

Address . . . . . . . . . . . . . . . . . . . . . . . . . . . . . . . . . . . . . . . . . . .

. . . . . . . . . . . . . . . . . . . . . . . . . . . . . . . . . . . . . . . . . . . . . . . . . .

. . . . . . . . . . . . . . . . . . . . . . . . . . . . . . . . . . . . . . . . . . . . . . . . . .

. . . . . . . . . . . . . . . . . . . . . Postcode . . . . . . . . . . . . . . . . . . .

Daytime Tel No . . . . . . . . . . . . . . . . . . . . . . . .   Valid to 31/12/01

## The Francis Frith Collectors' Guild

Please enrol me as a member for 12 months free of charge.

Name  Mr/Mrs/Ms . . . . . . . . . . . . . . . . . . . . . . . . . . . . . . . . . . . . . . . .

Address . . . . . . . . . . . . . . . . . . . . . . . . . . . . . . . . . . . . . . . . . . . . . . . .

. . . . . . . . . . . . . . . . . . . . . . . . . . . . . . . . . . . . . . . . . . . . . . . . . . . . . .

. . . . . . . . . . . . . . . . . . . . . . . . . . . . . . . . . . . . . . . . . . . . . . . . . . . . . .

. . . . . . . . . . . . . . . . . . . Postcode . . . . . . . . . . . . . . . . . .

Free Print - see overleaf

# Calculations

**3**

CAMBRIDGE
UNIVERSITY PRESS

PUBLISHED BY THE PRESS SYNDICATE OF THE UNIVERSITY OF CAMBRIDGE
The Pitt Building, Trumpington Street, Cambridge, United Kingdom

CAMBRIDGE UNIVERSITY PRESS
The Edinburgh Building, Cambridge CB2 2RU, UK  http://www.cup.cam.ac.uk
40 West 20th Street, New York, NY 10011–4211, USA  http://www.cup.org
10 Stamford Road, Oakleigh, Melbourne 3166, Australia
Ruiz de Alarcón 13, 28014 Madrid, Spain

First published 2000

Printed in the United Kingdom at the University Press, Cambridge

*Typefaces* Frutiger, Swift  *System* QuarkXPress 4.03®

*A catalogue record for this book is available from the British Library*

ISBN 0 521 78459 X paperback

Text illustration by Adam Stower

**General editors** for Cambridge Mathematics Direct
Sandy Cowling, Jane Crowden, Andrew King, Jeanette Mumford

**Writing team** for *Calculations 3*
Mark Adams, Sandy Cowling, Jenny Houssart, Lynn Huggins-Cooper,
Jeanette Mumford, Andrew King, Marian Reynolds, Fay Turner

The writers and publishers would like to thank the many schools and individuals
who trialled lessons for Cambridge Mathematics Direct.

Abbreviations and symbols
IP  Interactive picture
CM  Copymaster
A  is practice work
B  develops ideas
C  is extension work
★  if needed, helps with work in A

A red margin indicates that children work with the teacher.
A green margin indicates that children work independently.

# Contents

# Using addition and subtraction facts

| **Key idea** | If we know the answer to 6 + 7, we also know the answer to 7 + 6, 13 − 7 and 13 − 6. |

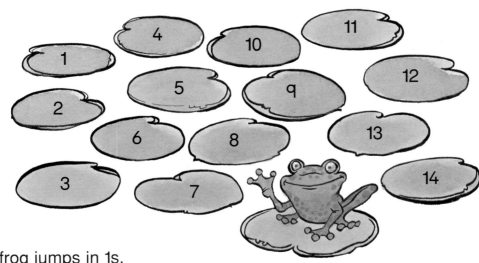

**A1** The frog jumps in 1s.

Fill in the missing numbers.

**a**  5 + △ = 12

   7 + △ = 12

   12 − 5 = △

   12 − 7 = △

**b**  4 + △ = 13

   △ + 8 = 13

   9 + △ = 13

   △ + 3 = 13

**A2** Find 3 jumps for each total.

Each way must be different.

Remember:
3 + 8 = 8 + 3 and
3 + 2 + 6 = 6 + 2 + 3

☐ + ☐ + ☐ = 12      ☐ + ☐ + ☐ = 13      ☐ + ☐ + ☐ = 14

☐ + ☐ + ☐ = 12      ☐ + ☐ + ☐ = 13      ☐ + ☐ + ☐ = 14

☐ + ☐ + ☐ = 12      ☐ + ☐ + ☐ = 13      ☐ + ☐ + ☐ = 14

**B1**   Copy and complete.

**a**  12 − 7 = ☐

12 − ☐ = 4

☐ − 6 = 6

**b**  13 − 4 = ☐

13 − ☐ = 12

☐ − 2 = 11

**c**  14 − 11 = ☐

14 − ☐ = 5

☐ − 8 = 6

**B2**   **Jumping round the pond**

**a**  The frog begins at 13.

Find its last jump to bring it back to 13.

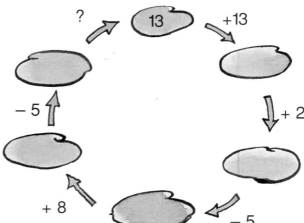

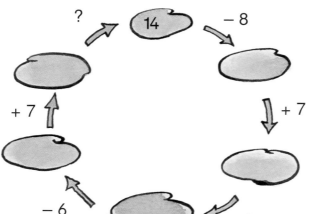

**b**  The frog begins at 14.

Find its last jump to bring it back to 14.

**C1**

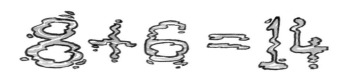

Investigate all the facts you can make from 8 + 6 = 14.

| **Key idea** | If we know the answer to 6 + 7, we also know the answer to 7 + 6, 13 − 7 and 13 − 6. |
|---|---|

# Undoing subtraction

| Key idea | Addition undoes subtraction. |
|----------|------------------------------|

**B1** Fill in the missing numbers.

a  15 – 7 = ☐

15 – 9 = ☐

15 – ☐ = 10

b  16 – 8 = ☐

16 – ☐ = 10

16 – 9 = ☐

c  17 – 6 = ☐

17 – 9 = ☐

17 – ☐ = 6

**B2** Copy and complete this addition grid.

| + | 7 | 8 | 9 | 10 |
|----|---|---|---|----|
| 6 | | | | |
| 7 | | | | |
| 8 | | | | |
| 9 | | . | | |
| 10 | | | | |
| 11 | | | | |

Use it to find the right answers to B1.

Tick your answers if they are right.

**B3** Write what you notice about the number patterns in the addition grid.

**C1** Do CM 3.

CM 3

Checking answers 1

| Key idea | We can check addition by adding numbers in a different order. |
|---|---|

**A1** Copy these. Fill in the missing numbers.

|   |   |
|---|---|
| 5 | 6 |
| 4 | 5 |

rows

$5 + 6 = \square$

$4 + 5 = \square$

columns

$5 + \square = \square$

$6 + \square = \square$

diagonals

$5 + \square = \square$

$4 + \square = \square$

**A2** Do these 2 x 2 grids in the same way.

|   |   |
|---|---|
| 7 | 8 |
| 6 | 7 |

|   |    |
|---|----|
| 9 | 10 |
| 8 | 9  |

Check your additions by comparing rows and columns.

**B1** You need your copy of CM 5.

Find this 3 x 3 grid in your addition triangle on CM 5.

Copy it. Fill in the missing numbers.

|   |   |   |
|---|---|---|
| 4 | 5 | 6 |
| 3 | 4 |   |
| 2 |   |   |

rows

$4 + 5 + 6 = \square$

$3 + 4 + \square = \square$

$2 + \square + \square = \square$

columns

$4 + 3 + 2 = \square$

$5 + 4 + \square = \square$

$2 + \square + \square = \square$

diagonals

$2 + 4 + 6 = \square$

$4 + 4 + \square = \square$

AS1 Number facts and strategies

CM 5

**B2**  Now do this 3 × 3 grid
in the same way.

| 5 | 6 | 7 |
|---|---|---|
|   |   |   |
| 3 |   | 5 |

Write what you notice about the totals of:

**a** the rows and columns,

**b** the diagonals.

**C1**  Find some 2 × 4 grids like these.

| 3 | 4 | 5 | 6 |
|---|---|---|---|
| 2 | 3 | 4 | 5 |

| 9 | 10 |
|---|---|
| 8 | 9 |
| 7 | 8 |
| 6 | 7 |

Investigate the totals of:

**a** each row and column,

**b** all the rows together and all the columns together.

---

**Key idea** | We can check addition by adding numbers in a different order.

# AS2.1 Using coins

| Key idea | We can write amounts of more than 100 pence (p) as pounds and pence, using a £ sign. |
|---|---|

**A1** Draw coins to make

a   35p      b   65p      c   £1.52      d   £1.06

**A2** This is your purse.

What would you buy?

Write down how much you spent in total.

You don't need to spend all your money.

**B1** Look at these shopping lists.

a
Jasbu
rubber
pen
crayons

b
Eleanor
stickers
pencil
badge
rubber

c
Morris
yo yo
pencil
badge
rubber

Draw coins to pay for each list.

Write down the total.

**B2**

Which 5 different coins make

a 86p          b £1.67          c £1.28

**C1** Investigate how many other amounts you can make with 5 different coins.

What if you can use any coin more than once?

| Key idea | We can write amounts of more than 100 pence (p) as pounds and pence, using a £ sign. |
|---|---|

# AS2.2 Finding totals

| Key idea | We can use what we know about tens to add money. |
|---|---|

**A1** Copy and fill in the boxes.

a 20 + 13 = ☐

b 30 + 15 = ☐

c 20 + 27 = ☐

d 33 + 40 = ☐

**A2**

Write down the cost of

a a Choc Bar and a Flying Saucer

b Space Rock Candy and 2 Fizz Bomb Lollies

c 2 packets of Coconut Ice and a Chew

d Raisins, Coconut Ice and a Fizz Bomb Lolly

**B1**

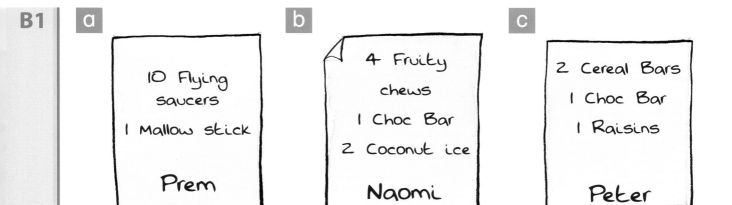

a. 10 Flying saucers
1 Mallow stick

Prem

b. 4 Fruity chews
1 Choc Bar
2 Coconut ice

Naomi

c. 2 Cereal Bars
1 Choc Bar
1 Raisins

Peter

Find the totals of the shopping lists.

Who spent more money, Peter or Naomi?

**C1**

You have up to £2 to spend on sweets and fruit for your friends.

Make a shopping list.

Is there any change from £2?

| Key idea | We can use what we know about tens to add money. |
| --- | --- |

# AS2.3 Solving problems using £.p

| Key idea | We can change pounds to pennies and pennies to pounds. |
|---|---|

**A1**    Cromar Caveman has a big bag of pennies.

How many will he need for

   **a**    Worm mousse?

   **b**    Coco-nut-ola?

MENU

| | |
|---|---|
| Worm mousse | £1.25 |
| Turtle eggs | £1.75 |
| Varanosaurus stew | £4.20 |
| Coco-nut-ola | £1.10 |
| Mammoth burger | £3.99 |
| Crispy fins | £1.80 |
| Pineapple fizz | £1.20 |
| Berry shake | £0.85 |

**A2**    He has 420p left. What can he buy?

**B1**    Write a number sentence to find the total cost of

   **a**    Crispy fins and Worm mousse,

   **b**    Varanosaurus stew and Crispy fins,

   **c**    Mammoth burger and Coco-nut-ola.

**B2**    Work with a partner.

Write a menu for The Caveman's Café.

Plan a meal for 2 for £10.

**C1**  Look at IP9.

**a**  Everyone at table 4 has Turtle eggs and Worm mousse.

Write the number sentence and find the total cost.

**b**  Everyone at table 2 has a Pineapple fizz and a Mammoth burger.

Write the number sentence and find the total cost.

**c**  Cromar has: Mammoth burger and Berry shake

Crog has: 6 Turtle eggs and Crispy fins

Crell has: Worm mousse and Coco-nut-ola

Write the number sentence and find the total cost.

**d**  Cromar buys Coco-nut-olas for 10 friends.

How much does he spend altogether?

Write the number sentence and find the total cost.

| Key idea | We can change pounds to pennies and pennies to pounds. |
| --- | --- |

# AS2.4 Giving change using £.p

**B1** Look at the orders.

Work out how much change for each table from £5.

**a**

1 Berry shake

1 Pineapple fizz

Table 2

**b**

2 Crispy fins

1 Berry shake

Table 3

**c**

3 Coco-nut-olas

Table 4

**B2** Each person on table 5 ordered a Coco-nut-ola, a Worm mousse and some Varanosaurus stew.

**a** What did each person pay?

**b** What was their change from £10?

**C1** You have £25 to feed the people at table 4.

What would you order?

How much change would you have?

# Adding 3 numbers

| Key idea | To add 3 or more numbers, look for pairs totalling 9, 10 or 11. |

**B1** Add the 3 numbers.

Show your working in a number sentence.

Put the largest number first.

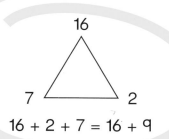

16 + 2 + 7 = 16 + 9

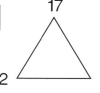 a

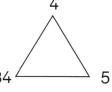 b

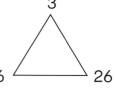 c

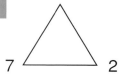 d

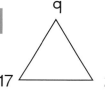 e

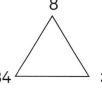 f

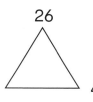 g

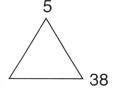 h

**B2** Choose 3 balls, one from each group.

Find the total.

Repeat with 3 different sets of balls.

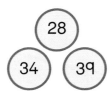

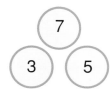

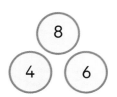

**C1** You need 2 sets of 0 – 9 digit cards.

Shuffle them.

Deal 4. Find the total.

Record in a number sentence.

Deal 5, then 6, then 7, ...

Each time find the total and record.

# AS3.2 Splitting numbers for adding

| **Key idea** | Splitting numbers into '5 and a bit' can help us add to numbers ending in 5. |

**A1** Use '5 and a bit' to find these answers.

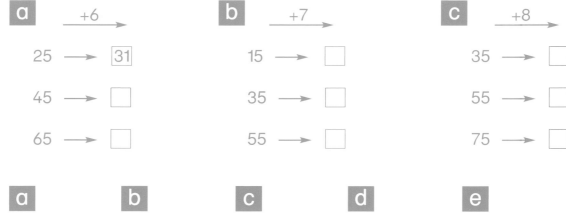

**a** +6

25 ⟶ 31

45 ⟶ ☐

65 ⟶ ☐

**b** +7

15 ⟶ ☐

35 ⟶ ☐

55 ⟶ ☐

**c** +8

35 ⟶ ☐

55 ⟶ ☐

75 ⟶ ☐

**B1**

**a** 43 **b** 52 **c** 59 **d** 64 **e** 81

Find the 2 letters for each house.

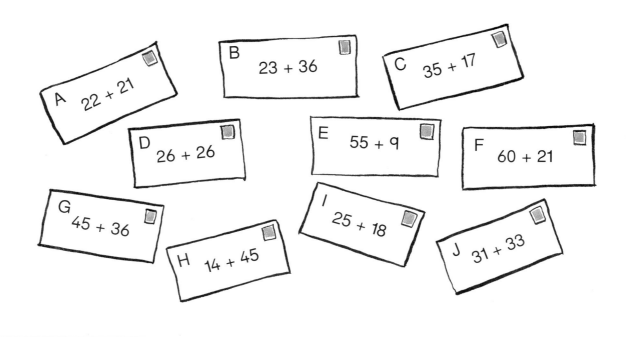

A 22 + 21

B 23 + 36

C 35 + 17

D 26 + 26

E 55 + 9

F 60 + 21

G 45 + 36

H 14 + 45

I 25 + 18

J 31 + 33

**B2**  For letters C, E, F, G:

**a**  Draw an empty number line.

Record your method on it like this.

**Example**    Letter I   25 + 18 = 43

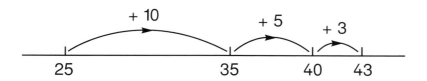

**b**  Check your answers to **a** with another method.

Draw an empty number line.

Record your check method on it like this.

**Example**    Letter I   25 + 18 = 43

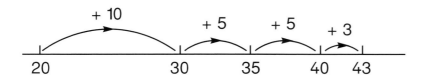

**C1**  Make up one more letter sum for each house.

| **Key idea** | Splitting numbers into '5 and a bit' can help us add to numbers ending in 5. |
|---|---|

# AS3.3  Adding 11, 21, 31, ...

| Key idea | We can use what we know about adding 11 to add 21, 31, ... |
|---|---|

**A1** Copy and complete this grid.

|  | 9 | 17 | 26 | 35 | 48 |
|---|---|---|---|---|---|
| add 11 | 20 |  |  |  |  |
| add 21 |  | 38 |  |  |  |
| add 31 |  |  | 57 |  |  |

**A2** Carry these patterns on. Stop at 95.

**a** 
$14 + 11 = \square$

$24 + 11 = \square$

$34 + 11 = \square$

44...

**b** 
$14 + 21 = \square$

$24 + 21 = \square$

$34 + 21 = \square$

44...

**c** 
$14 + 31 = \square$

$24 + 31 = \square$

$34 + 31 = \square$

44...

**B1** Copy these grids. Use the clues to solve the puzzles.

**a**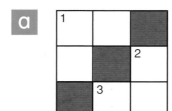

**b**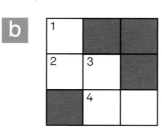

across | down
--- | ---
1   41 + 27 | 1   51 + 18
3   61 + 34 | 2   71 + 24

across | down
--- | ---
2   46 + 41 | 1   27 + 31
4   81 + 16 | 3   28 + 51

**C1** Do CM 10.

AS3 More strategies and patterns

CM
10

Subtracting 11, 21, 31, ...

| Key idea | We can use what we know about subtracting 11 to subtract 21, 31, ... |

**A1** Continue these patterns as far as you can go.

**a** 100 – 11 = 89

89 – 11 = ☐

78 – 11 = ☐

**b** 99 – 21 = 78

78 – 21 = ☐

57 – 21 = ☐

**c** 98 – 31 = 67

67 – 31 = ☐

**A2** Write what you notice about each pattern in A1.

**B1** Copy and complete these patterns.

**a** 97 – 11 = ☐

97 – 21 = ☐

97 – 31 = ☐

**b** 86 – 11 = ☐

86 – 21 = ☐

86 – 31 = ☐

**c** 71 – 11 = ☐

71 – 21 = ☐

71 – 31 = ☐

**d** 90 – 11 = ☐

90 – 21 = ☐

90 – 31 = ☐

Use the patterns to find

97 – 71 = ☐     86 – 61 = ☐     71 – 51 = ☐     90 – 71 = ☐

**B2** In this yacht race, each pair of sails has a difference of 25.

Find the missing numbers.

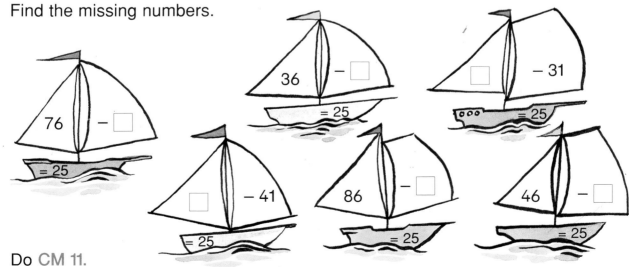

**C1** Do **CM 11**.

CM 11

Adding and subtracting 9, 19, 29, ...

| Key idea | We can use what we know about adding or subtracting 9 to add or subtract 19, 29, ... |
| --- | --- |

| 1 | 2 | 3 | 4 | 5 | 6 | 7 | 8 | 9 | 10 |
| 11 | | | | | | | | | |
| 21 | | | | | | | | | 30 |
| 31 | | | | | | | | | |
| 41 | | | | | | | | | 50 |
| | | | | | | | | | |
| 61 | | | | | | | | | |
| 71 | | | | | | | | | 80 |
| | | | | | | | | | |
| 91 | | | | | | | | | |

**A1**

Copy and complete this table.

| Caterpillar | head | tail |
| --- | --- | --- |
| a | 22 | 13 |
| b | | |
| c | | |
| d | | |
| e | | |
| f | | |
| g | | |
| h | | |
| i | | |

Use your table to find these missing numbers.

a  $13 + \square = 22$

b  $25 + 19 = \square$

c  $\square - 19 = 17$

d  $52 + 29 = \square$

e  $48 + \square = 77$

f  $\square - 9 = \square$

g  $93 - 19 = \square$

h  $66 + \square = 85$

i  $\square + 9 = \square$

# Using patterns

| Key idea | We can find patterns and use them to calculate. |
| --- | --- |

**A1** Write the numbers that the letters a, b, c, d, e, f and g represent in this addition square.

| + | 5 | 6 | 7 | 8 | 9 |
| --- | --- | --- | --- | --- | --- |
| 5 | | | | a | |
| 6 | | b | | | |
| 7 | c | | | d | |
| 8 | | | | | e |
| 9 | | | f | | g |

**B1** Continue each pattern for 5 rows.

**a**   $99 - 11 = 88$

$88 - 11 = \square$

$77 - \square = \square$

**b**   $99 - 9 = 90 \longrightarrow 9 + 0 = 9$

$90 - 9 = 81 \longrightarrow 8 + 1 = 9$

$\square - 9 = \square \longrightarrow \square + \square = \square$

**B2** Copy and continue these patterns for 2 rows more.

**a**   $16 + 3 = 19$

$16 + 13 = 29$

$16 + 23 = \square$

**b**   $79 - 5 = 74$

$79 - 15 = \square$

$79 - 25 = \square$

**c**   $14 + 5 = \square$

$24 + 5 = \square$

$34 + 5 = \square$

Now use each pattern to work out

$16 + 73 = \square$     $79 - 65 = \square$     $94 + 5 = \square$

## C1 | Walls and windows

You need interlocking cubes.

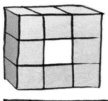 A wall with 1 window needs 8 bricks.

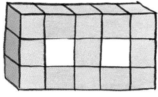 A wall with 2 windows needs 13 bricks.

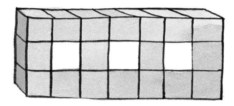 A wall with 3 windows needs 18 bricks.

**a** Build a wall with 4 windows, then a wall with 5 windows.

**b** Complete this table.

| windows | bricks |
|---------|--------|
| 1 | 8 |
| 2 | |
| 3 | |
| 4 | |
| 5 | |
| 6 | |
| ⋮ | ⋮ |
| 8 | |
| ⋮ | ⋮ |
| 10 | |

**c** Use the pattern in the table to find the number of bricks for:

6 windows

8 windows

10 windows

**d** Explain how the pattern works.

| Key idea | We can find patterns and use them to calculate. |
|----------|------------------------------------------------|

# 54.1 Finding doubles

| Key idea | Using doubles is quicker than counting on in 1s. |
|---|---|

**★1** You need

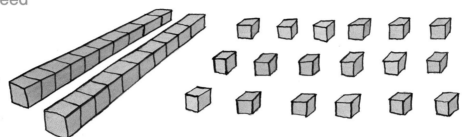

Find these doubles.

| a | 5 + 5 | b | 6 + 6 | c | 8 + 8 | d | 11 + 11 |
|---|---|---|---|---|---|---|---|
| e | 9 + 9 | f | 12 + 12 | g | 15 + 15 | h | 16 + 16 |

**A1** Draw a number line to do each double.

Mark all your jumps along it.

| a | 12 + 12 | b | 15 + 15 | c | 20 + 20 |
|---|---|---|---|---|---|
| d | 18 + 18 | e | 17 + 17 | f | 19 + 19 |

**A2** Do CM 14.

**B1** Play with a partner.

You need 1 set of 1–20 number cards between you.

Shuffle them and put them in rows face down.

Take turns to turn over 2 cards.

Keep the pair of cards if one card is the double of the other.

If not, turn the pair face down again.

The winner is the player with the biggest number of pairs.

**B2** Look for patterns to help you find the doubles.

| a | 4 → 8 | b | 6 → ☐ | c | 9 → ☐ |
|---|---|---|---|---|---|
|   | 14 → ☐ |   | 16 → ☐ |   | 19 → ☐ |

| d | 11 → ☐ | e | 5 → ☐ | f | 7 → ☐ |
|---|---|---|---|---|---|
|   | 21 → ☐ |   | 15 → ☐ |   | 17 → ☐ |
|   | 31 → ☐ |   | 25 → ☐ |   | 27 → ☐ |

**C1** Draw a number line to show how you did 27 + 27.

Can you find another way using the number line?

**C2** Choose some bigger numbers to double.

| Key idea | Using doubles is quicker than counting on in 1s. |
|---|---|

AS4 Doubles

# Near doubles

| **Key idea** | Use doubles to help add 2 numbers that are near to each other. |

Copy and fill in the boxes.

**A1**   **a** 12 + 12 = ☐     **b** 12 + 13 = ☐     **c** 11 + 12 = ☐

**A2**   **a** 14 + 14 = ☐     **b** 14 + 15 = ☐     **c** 14 + 13 = ☐

**A3**   **a** 17 + 17 = ☐     **b** 17 + 16 = ☐     **c** 18 + 17 = ☐

**A4**   **a** 18 + 18 = ☐     **b** 19 + 18 = ☐     **c** 17 + 18 = ☐

**A5**   Find near doubles to make these sentences true.

    **a** ☐ + 11 = 21     **b** ☐ + ☐ = 31

**B1**   Use doubling to do these.

Write down the answer and the number you doubled.

    **a** 11 + 13     **b** 10 + 12     **c** 13 + 15

    **d** 11 + 15     **e** 12 + 16     **f** 14 + 18

**B2** Find 2 ways to do these.

Show your working on a number line.

**a** 15 + 17 = ☐  **b** 17 + 19 = ☐

**c** 15 + 19 = ☐  **d** 16 + 20 = ☐

**C1**

Let's split the difference.

$$14 + 18 = 16 + 16$$
$$= 32$$

Use divers' doubles to do these; split the difference!

**a** 12 + 16   **b** 13 + 17   **c** 15 + 19   **d** 23 + 27

**C2** Can you split the difference and use doubles to add these pairs?

**a** 25, 35   **b** 32, 48   **c** 29, 41

Be ready to explain how you did it.

| **Key idea** | Use doubles to help add 2 numbers that are near to each other. |
|---|---|

# Doubling multiples of 5

| **Key idea** | We can double 5, 15, 25, ... by doubling the tens and adding 10. |
|---|---|

**B1** How much for 2?

a £75

b £46

c £54

d £85

e £96

**B2** Bags of money

The amount in each new money bag is the sum of the 2 bags below it.

35p

15p   20p

15p + 20p = 35p

Copy and complete these money bags.

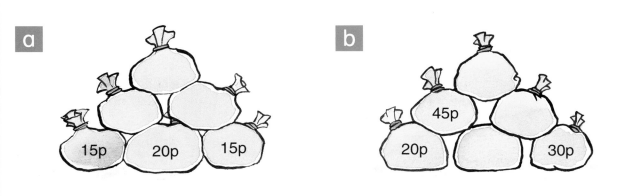

a   15p   20p   15p

b   45p   20p   30p

Turn over for c and d.

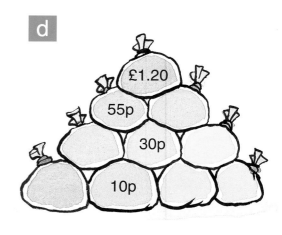

c

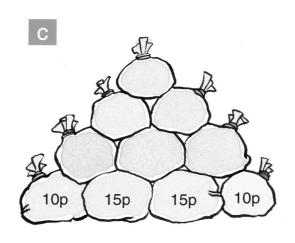

10p  15p  15p  10p

d

£1.20
55p
30p
10p

**C1**  Copy and complete these money bags.

a

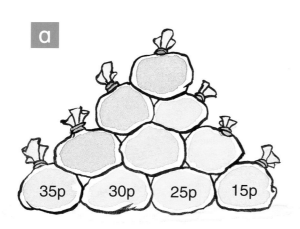

35p  30p  25p  15p

b

£1.85

**C2**  Draw your own piles of money bags with 4 bags at the bottom.

Use 5p, 10p, 15p and 20p in the bottom row.

Change the order of the amounts.

Investigate what happens to the amount at the top.

| Key idea | We can double 5, 15, 25, ... by doubling the tens and adding 10. |

# 4.5 Doubling and halving

| Key idea | We can check halving with doubling. |
|---|---|

**A1** Share the treasure between 2 divers.

Write down each diver's share.

Double your answer to check.

**a** 24 gold rings

**b** 36 silver spoons

**c** 32 goblets

**d** 28 candlesticks

**A2** Copy and complete.

| Money bag A | Money bag B | Total money | Half share |
|---|---|---|---|
| 12 | 14 | 26 | 13 |
| 18 | 20 | | |
| 24 | 26 | | |
| 33 | 37 | | |
| 41 | 39 | | |
| 66 | 64 | | |
| 79 | 81 | | |
| 95 | 97 | | |

**B1** Fill in the boxes.

$$10 \xleftarrow{\text{halve}} 20 \xrightarrow{\text{double}} 40 \qquad \text{Check} \qquad 10 \xrightarrow{\text{double}} 20$$
$$40 \xrightarrow{\text{halve}} 20$$

$$\square \xleftarrow{\text{halve}} 40 \xrightarrow{\text{double}} \square \qquad \text{Check} \qquad 20 \xrightarrow{\text{double}} \square$$
$$80 \xrightarrow{\text{halve}} \square$$

$$\square \xleftarrow{} 60 \xrightarrow{} \square \qquad \text{Check} \qquad \square \xrightarrow{} \square$$
$$\square \xrightarrow{} \square$$

$$\square \xleftarrow{} 70 \xrightarrow{} \square \qquad \text{Check} \qquad \square \xrightarrow{} \square$$
$$\square \xrightarrow{} \square$$

$$\square \xleftarrow{} 90 \xrightarrow{} \square \qquad \text{Check} \qquad \square \xrightarrow{} \square$$
$$\square \xrightarrow{} \square$$

**C1** Investigate adding multiples of 5 that end in 5.

Record your results like this.

| add | total | half of total |
|-----|-------|---------------|
| 25 + 35 | 60 | 30 |
| 25 + 45 | | |
| 35 + 45 | | |
| 55 + 65 | | |
| 65 + 85 | | |
| 75 + 85 | | |
| 75 + 95 | | |

**C2** Discuss quick ways to add numbers such as 35 + 55 and 65 + 85.

| **Key idea** | We can check halving with doubling. |
|---|---|

# Adding one digit to a 2-digit number

| Key idea | We can use the next ten to split a number into chunks for adding. |

$$14 \rightarrow 20 \qquad 32 \rightarrow 40$$

$$28 \rightarrow 30$$

**A1**

**a** $14 + 7 = \square$

**b** $17 + 7 = \square$

**c** $28 + 6 = \square$

**d** $25 + 8 = \square$

**e** $32 + 9 = \square$

**f** $36 + 8 = \square$

**B1**

$$17 + \square = 25$$

$$17 + 8 = 25$$

**a** $29 + \square = 34$

**b** $\square + 26 = 36$

**c** $\square + 25 = 33$

**d** $38 + \square = 47$

**e** $46 + \square = 51$

**f** $48 + \square = 54$

**g** $67 + \square = 74$

**h** $77 + \square = 82$

| Key idea | We can find lots of pairs of multiples of 5 that total 100. |
|---|---|

**A1**

**a** 65 + ☐ = 100

**b** 25 + ☐ = 100

**c** 70 + ☐ = 100

**d** 85 + ☐ = 100

**e** 95 + ☐ = 100

**f** 90 + ☐ = 100

**g** 55 + ☐ = 100

**h** 75 + ☐ = 100

**i** 50 + ☐ = 100

| 0 | 1 | 2 | 3 | 4 | 5 | 6 | 7 | 8 | 9 |
|---|---|---|---|---|---|---|---|---|---|
| 10 | 11 | 12 | 13 | 14 | 15 | 16 | 17 | 18 | 19 |
| 20 | 21 | 22 | 23 | 24 | 25 | 26 | 27 | 28 | 29 |
| 30 | 31 | 32 | 33 | 34 | 35 | 36 | 37 | 38 | 39 |
| 40 | 41 | 42 | 43 | 44 | 45 | 46 | 47 | 48 | 49 |
| 50 | 51 | 52 | 53 | 54 | 55 | 56 | 57 | 58 | 59 |
| 60 | 61 | 62 | 63 | 64 | 65 | 66 | 67 | 68 | 69 |
| 70 | 71 | 72 | 73 | 74 | 75 | 76 | 77 | 78 | 79 |
| 80 | 81 | 82 | 83 | 84 | 85 | 86 | 87 | 88 | 89 |
| 90 | 91 | 92 | 93 | 94 | 95 | 96 | 97 | 98 | 99 |
| 100 | | | | | | | | | |

**B1**

**a** ☐ + 15 = 100

**b** ☐ + 30 = 100

**c** ☐ + 25 = 100

**d** ☐ + 40 = 100

**e** ☐ + 45 = 100

**f** ☐ + 60 = 100

**B2** Can you find 3 different solutions for △ + ☐ = 100?

# Subtracting one digit from a 2-digit number

| Key idea | We can jump to the tens number below to subtract a number in 2 chunks. |
| --- | --- |

**A1** Each jar contains a different number of biscuits.

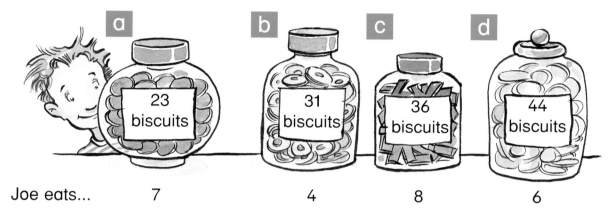

| a | b | c | d |
| --- | --- | --- | --- |
| 23 biscuits | 31 biscuits | 36 biscuits | 44 biscuits |

Joe eats...      7        4        8        6

How many biscuits are left in each jar?
Use a number line to help you.

**A2** There were 32 biscuits in this box.

How many did Bilal eat if there are:

a 28 left?    b 24 left?    c 27 left?    d 25 left?

**B1** If Charlene eats 6 Jammy Dodgers and there are 29 left,
how many were in the box when she started?

**B2** This box has 45 delicious biscuits in it.

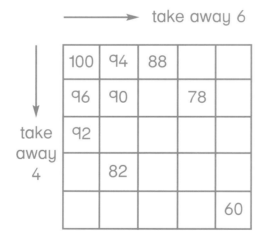

Make up 4 'biscuit problems' about it.

**C1** Copy this grid. Work out all the missing numbers.

take away 6 →

| | take away 6 | | | |
|---|---|---|---|---|
| 100 | 94 | 88 | | |
| 96 | 90 | | 78 | |
| 92 | | | | |
| | 82 | | | |
| | | | | 60 |

take away 4 ↓

Write about any patterns you can see.

# Combining multiples of 10 and 2-digit numbers

| Key idea | We can use our knowledge of counting in 10s to add or subtract a multiple of 10. |
|---|---|

Draw number lines to record B and C.
Write a number sentence under each line.

**B1**

a 90 + 30 = ☐

b 80 + 50 = ☐

c 130 − 50 = ☐

d 160 − 80 = ☐

e 120 − ☐ = 60

f 140 − ☐ = 90

**B2**

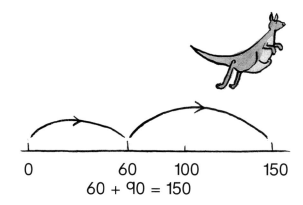

60 + 90 = 150

a Take 2 jumps from 0 to 150.

b Take 2 different jumps from 0 to 150.

c Choose a different number to finish on.

Take 2 jumps from 0.

**C1** Take 3 jumps from 0.
Choose your finishing number.

0

# Combining pairs of 2-digit numbers

| Key idea | There are lots of good strategies to use when we add or subtract any pair of 2-digit numbers. |
|---|---|

**B1**

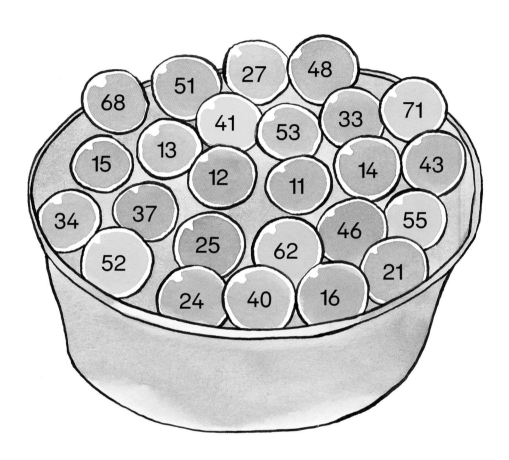

Choose pairs of numbers from the ball pond to make some number sentences.
Add or subtract.

Here is one to get you started.        33 + 14 = 47

Be careful when you do subtraction sentences!
Which number do you put first?

**C1**        △ + ☐ = 57

Find pairs of numbers to put in the boxes.

Linking addition and subtraction

| Key idea | We can write a subtraction sentence for every addition sentence. |

**C1** Trios

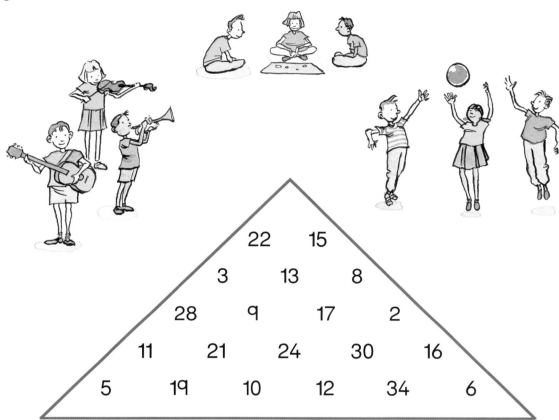

22    15
  3      13      8
28      9      17      2
11      21      24      30      16
5      19      10      12      34      6

**a** Choose 3 numbers from the triangle to make an addition sentence like this.

11 + 2 = 13

How many trios can you find?

**b** Look at each sentence you have made.
Use the trio to write 3 more number sentences like this.

11 + 2 = 13        2 + 11 = 13

13 − 2 = 11        13 − 11 = 2

# Adding single digits to 3-digit numbers

| **Key idea** | It is easy to add hundreds numbers to single digits if we start from the hundreds number. |
| --- | --- |

**A1** **As easy as 1, 2, 3!**

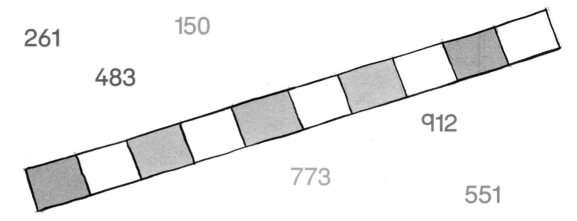

261

150

483

912

773

551

Use the counting stick.
Add 3 to each number.
Write down the answer.

**A2** You need a dice.

Use the same numbers again.
Throw the dice and add your score.

**B1** Copy and fill in the missing numbers.

| a | 321 + 6 = ☐ | | b | 201 + 8 = ☐ |

| c | 642 + ☐ = 649 | | d | 102 + ☐ = 108 |

| e | 483 + ☐ = 487 | | f | 501 + ☐ = 505 |

**B2** a Explain how you did B1 a.

b Explain how you did B1 c.

# Adding 3 large numbers

| Key idea | To add 3 numbers, look for pairs that are easy to add first. |
|---|---|

**A1** | **Pure gold!**

Work with a partner.
Use nuggets and ingots to help you add.
Write a number sentence for each one.

a   23 + 41 + 10        b   77 + 1 + 10

c   52 + 22 + 20        d   41 + 33 + 25

e   41 + 6 + 44         f   15 + 35 + 26

g   8 + 58 + 19         h   42 + 42 + 42

**B1** | You may like to use a number line.

Add 3 of the numbers.

          42        121        11        95        68

Find all the different totals.
Write a number sentence for each one.

**B2** | Choose a number sentence from B1.
Use it to make up a number story.

**C1** | You need 3 dice.

Throw 3 dice 3 times.
Make three 3-digit numbers.
Find different ways to add them.
Record each way.

# Subtracting single digits from 3-digit numbers

| Key idea | We can count back to subtract a single digit from 3-digit numbers. |
|---|---|

**A1** | Count back!

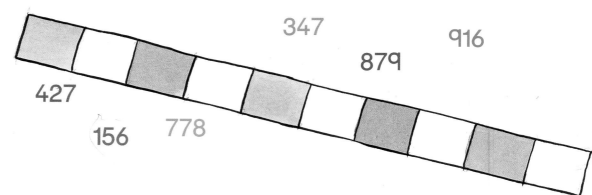

Use the counting stick.
Take 5 away from each number.
Write down the answer.

**A2** | You need a dice.

Use the same numbers again.
Throw the dice and subtract your score.

**B1** | Copy and fill in the missing numbers.

a | 329 – 3 = ☐

b | 288 – 7 = ☐

c | 515 – ☐ = 510

d | 857 – ☐ = 851

e | ☐ + 4 = 436

f | ☐ + 8 = 669

**B2** | a Explain how you did B1 c.

b Explain how you did B1 e.

Why not use a number line to explain?

# Finding differences

| Key idea | Count on from the smaller to the larger number to find the difference between numbers that are close together. |

108 cm — Esther
109 cm — Ruth
111 cm — Andrew
117 cm — Daisy
121 cm — Declan
123 cm — James

123 cm
106 cm

**A1** **a** Who is 10 cm taller than Andrew?

**b** Who is 2 cm taller than Ruth?

Use the ruler to help you count on.

**A2** Find Esther.
How much shorter is she than each of the other children?

**B1** Jasmine joins the class. She is 115 cm tall.
How much taller or shorter are the other children than her?

## Skyscrapers

Here are some of the tallest buildings in the world.

CN Tower, Toronto, Canada                       555 m

World Financial Centre, Shanghai                460 m

Petronas Towers, Kuala Lumpur                   452 m

Sears Tower, Chicago, USA                       443 m

World Trade Centre, New York, USA               417 m

What are the differences in height between all the buildings?
Think of a way to record all of them clearly.

| **Key idea** | Count on from the smaller to the larger number to find the difference between numbers that are close together. |
|---|---|

AS6 Introducing strategies for 3-digit numbers

More differences

| Key idea | We can make jumps of different sizes when we are counting on or back to find a difference. |

**1**

You need a dice with 4, 5, 6, 7, 8, 9.

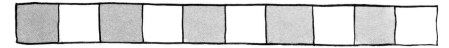

Start at 100.
Throw your dice. Write down your throw.
Count back. Write down where you landed.
100        4              96
Throw again. Have 10 throws.

**A1**  Find the difference between 300 and

[a] 295        [b] 297        [c] 291        [d] 308

Count on or back.

**A2**  Find the missing numbers.
Count on or back.

Jump to the
hundreds number in
the middle first

[a] 198 + ☐ = 203        [b] 203 – 198 = ☐

[c] 396 + ☐ = 403        [d] 403 – 396 = ☐

[e] 582 + ☐ = 607        [f] 607 – 582 = ☐

**B1**  Find pairs of 3-digit numbers with a difference of 9.

[a] Write number sentences like this.

Find 'nice' numbers
to jump to.

308 – 299 = 9

[b] Write about any patterns you see.

| Key idea | We can make jumps of different sizes when we are counting on or back to find a difference. |

# AS7.1 Adding and subtracting 10

| Key idea | We can add or subtract 9 and 11 to or from a hundreds number easily, by adding or subtracting 10. |
|---|---|

What are the output numbers in the function machines?

**A1**

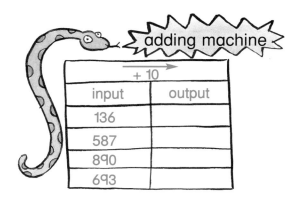

adding machine

**+ 10**

| input | output |
|---|---|
| 136 | |
| 587 | |
| 890 | |
| 693 | |

going down

**− 10**

| input | output |
|---|---|
| 287 | |
| 396 | |
| 514 | |
| 803 | |

**A2**

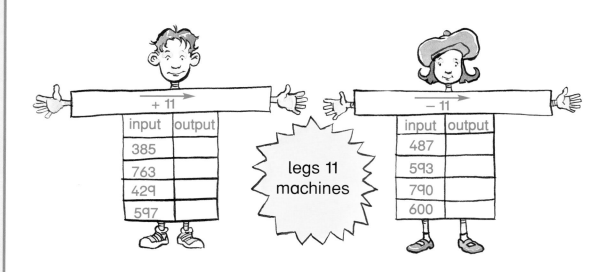

**+ 11**

| input | output |
|---|---|
| 385 | |
| 763 | |
| 429 | |
| 597 | |

legs 11 machines

**− 11**

| input | output |
|---|---|
| 487 | |
| 593 | |
| 790 | |
| 600 | |

**A3** Draw your own function machines for + 9 and − 9.

+ 9 : input     138      446      781      695

− 9 : input     742      386      501      700

CM 22

**B1** These children have lots of stickers.

They buy 10 more each.
How many do they have now?

Write a number sentence for each child.

**B2** A cake maker has a box of 500 candles.

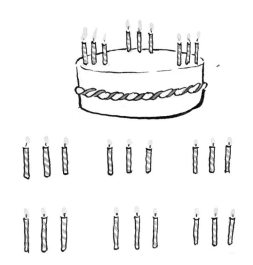

She makes a cake and puts 9 candles on it.
How many are left in the box?

She makes another 9th birthday cake.
How many candles are left now?

How many will be left if she uses 9 more?
Can you continue the pattern?

**C1** **The 501 down challenge**

You need a dice marked with numbers 9, 9, 10, 10, 11, 11.

Start with a score of 501.

Throw the dice and subtract the number
you throw from your score.

Write your new score underneath.

Carry on – throw the dice
     subtract the number you throw
     write down the new score.

Stop when you pass 400.

You could race
against the clock.

| Key idea | We can add or subtract 9 and 11 to or from a hundreds number easily, by adding or subtracting 10. |
|---|---|

# AS7.2 Adding hundreds

| Key idea | When we add 100 to a number, the tens and units digits stay the same. |
|---|---|

**A1** Help the shopkeeper work out how many toys he has.
Write a number sentence for each one.

|  | In the cupboard | In the shop |
|---|---|---|
|  | 1 box of 100 | 65 |
|  | 3 boxes of 100 | 48 |
|  | 5 boxes of 100 | 32 |

**A2** The shopkeeper looks at his list of joke toys.

He orders 100 more of each one.

How many will he have now?

Write a number sentence for each toy.

### Jokes-on-us Ltd Stock List

Fake sugar   439

Ink blots   285

Squirters   587

Stink bombs   643

Hand buzzers   430

**A3** Write a number for each spider to make these number sentences true.

231 + 100 = 🕷          100 + 🕷 = 365          423 − 100 = 🕷

🕷 + 100 = 893          210 − 100 = 🕷          🕷  100 = 🕷

Make up your own number sentences with +100 or −100.

**B1**  The shopkeeper has sold a lot of toys this week.
Work out how many he has now.

| | boxes | on display | total |
|---|---|---|---|
| spiders | 1 | 43 | a |
| snakes | 3 | 27 | b |
| whoopee cushions | 4 | 86 | c |

**B2**  **a**  There are 386 flower hats.
The shopkeeper gives 100 to the school
to sell at the fete.

How many are left?
Write a number sentence.

**b**  He gives away more hats and writes it all down.
Help him to fill in the chart.

| | number to start with | given away | total left |
|---|---|---|---|
| pirate hat | 492 | 100 | |
| clown hat | 573 | 100 | |
| police helmet | | 100 | 296 |
| bowler hat | | 100 | 445 |
| straw hat | 683 | | 583 |

**C1**  Copy this grid.
Look for the patterns.
Fill in the empty squares.

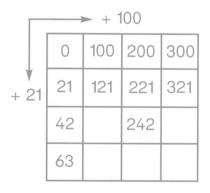

+ 100

| 0 | 100 | 200 | 300 |
| 21 | 121 | 221 | 321 |
| 42 | | 242 | |
| 63 | | | |

+ 21

Make up some more grids like these.

| **Key idea** | When we add 100 to a number the tens and units digits stay the same. |
|---|---|

Working to 1000

| Key idea | We can use pairs of numbers that total 10 to help us learn pairs that total 1000. |

**A1** Popcorn is served using a scoop that holds 100 g.
1 kg (1000 g) of popcorn is split into 2 tubs using the scoop.

Here is one way of doing this.

This can be written as an addition.   600 g + 400 g = 1000 g

Find different ways of splitting 1000 g into 2 tubs using the 100 g scoop.
Write the addition to match each way you find.

**A2** Fizzy drinks are sold in 3 sizes.

Find the totals.    **a** 400 ml + 500 ml    **b** 500 ml + 700 ml

Find the differences.    **c** 500 ml – 400 ml    **d** 700 ml – 400 ml

**B1** This jug holds 1500 ml of drink.

Arash pours out 300 ml.

How much is left in the jug?

Use pairs of numbers
that total 10 to help.

**B2**   How much is left when he pours out these amounts from the full jug?

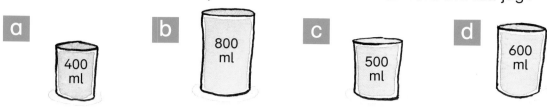

**a** 400 ml    **b** 800 ml    **c** 500 ml    **d** 600 ml

**B3**   This time 1300 ml is left in the jug.

How much did Emily pour out?

1300 ml

**B4**   How much did she pour out of these jugs?
They all started with 1500 ml.

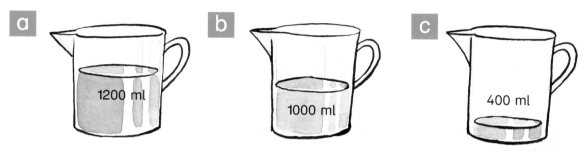

**a** 1200 ml    **b** 1000 ml    **c** 400 ml

**C1**   **Target 1500**

You need a dice marked with the numbers 100, 100, 200, 200, 300, 300.

Throw the dice and write down your score.

Throw again and add your new score to the old one.

Keep throwing and adding on your new score till you reach 1500.

If your score brings the total over 1500 it does not count.

Throw again until you reach 1500 exactly.

Play Target 2000 with a dice marked 100, 200, 300, 400, 500, 600.

Try other games with larger targets and larger dice numbers.

| Key idea | We can use pairs of numbers that total 10 to help us learn pairs that total 100. |
|---|---|

| Key idea | We can use an empty number line to help us add 2-digit numbers. |

**A1** You need a quadnumber card from CM 27.

a Add one of the numbers on your quadnumber card to 67.
Draw an empty number line to help you.

b Repeat for each of the other numbers.

**A2** a Add the numbers on your quadnumber card to make 4 more numbers.

b Add each of the numbers you made in A2 a to 37.
Draw an empty number line to help you.

**B1** a Add the numbers on your quadnumber card to make 4 numbers.
This time you can use each number more than once to make larger numbers

b Add these numbers to 75. Draw an empty number line to help you.

**C1** Choose another quadnumber card.

Use the numbers on it to make numbers to add to 89.

Draw an empty number line to help you.

# Using an empty number line for HTU + HTU

| Key idea | We can use an empty number line to help us add any numbers. |
|---|---|

**1** The shark is eating some fish
Then he eats some more.

Find out how many altogether.

**a** 21 + 10 = ☐

+ 10

21

**b** 32 + 16 = ☐

+ 10

32        42

**c** 35 + 23 = ☐

+ 10      + 10

35        45

**d** 43 + 54 = ☐

43

**2**  **a** 323 + 100 = ☐

+ 100

323

**b** 234 + 20 = ☐

234

**c** 146 + 3 = ☐

146

**d** 256 + 111 = ☐

256

**A1** Add in your head.

Draw your method on an empty number line.

**a** 28 + 61 = ☐

**b** 23 + 39 = ☐

**c** 78 + 17 = ☐

**d** 63 + 59 = ☐

**A2** Use the empty number line to add these.

**a** 126 + 200 = ☐

+ 100    + 100

126

**b** 239 + 40 = ☐

**c** 132 + 145 = ☐

**d** 305 + 174 = ☐

**B1** Find pairs of numbers that add to make 475.

Use an empty number line to record like this.

+ 100    + 100

275          475       275 + 200 = 475

| Key idea | We can use an empty number line to help us add any numbers. |

AS8 Developing jottings for addition

# Introducing columns

| Key idea | When we add numbers, we can write them in columns to help us remember what we are doing. |

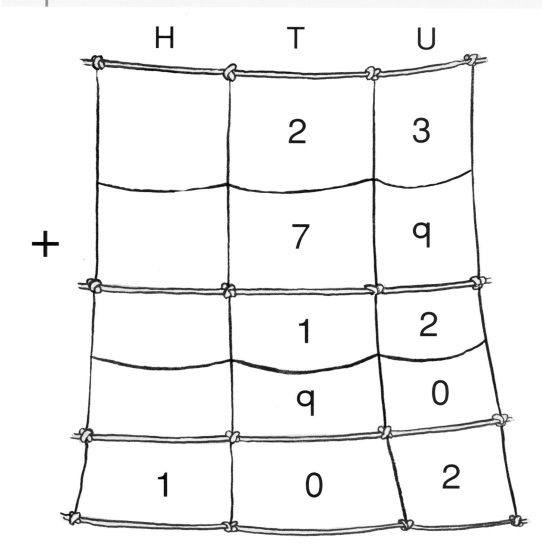

**A1** Do CM 29.

**A2** Record these additions in columns.

**a** 34 + 45 = ☐  **b** 63 + 39 = ☐

**c** 98 + 21 = ☐  **d** 58 + 76 = ☐

**B1** There are lots of bags of coins like these around the wrecked ship.

2 divers bring back 10 bags each.
They cannot hold more than three 100s bags each.

The first diver gets some 100s, some 10s and some 1s.
The second diver gets some 10s and some 1s.

Find how many coins they could bring back altogether.

Record your ways in columns like this.

```
Diver 1        1  3  6
Diver 2    +      2  8
                  ──────
                  1  4
                  5  0
               1  0  0
                  ──────
               1  6  4
```

**C1** The divers try again.
They each get 10 bags with 100s, 10s and 1s.

How much could they bring back this time?

**Key idea** When we add numbers, we can write them in columns to help us remember what we are doing.

# Introducing columns for subtraction

| Key idea | We can take away numbers by splitting them into tens and units. |
|---|---|

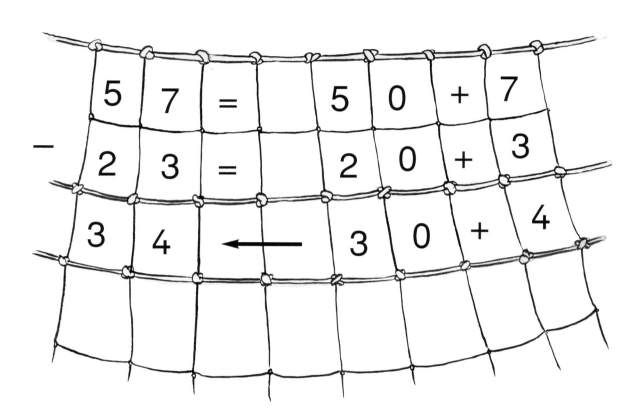

**B1** Work in columns.

**a**
```
    8 6 =  ☐ + ☐
  − 7 4 =  ☐ + ☐
  _____  _____
       ←    ☐ + ☐
```

**b**
```
    6 8 =
  − 2 2 =
  _____
       ←
```

**c**
```
    9 9 =
  − 3 3 =
  _____
       ←
```

**d**
```
    7 5 =
  − 3 5 =
  _____
       ←
```

**B2**  Work in columns.

a  63 – 11     b  97 – 53     c  78 – 56     d  49 – 17

**B3**  In the treasure box there are

96 necklaces
78 rings
35 gold chains
59 silver buckles

The diver collects

21 necklaces
56 rings
12 gold chains
41 silver buckles

a  Work in columns.
Find out how much treasure there is left in the box.

b  Make up your own 'treasure' subtraction.
Use what is left in the box now.

Take care to line up the units under units and tens under tens.

**C1**  Work in columns.

a  196 – 82     b  275 – 65     c  148 – 33

| Key idea | We can take away numbers by splitting them into tens and units. |

Subtracting in columns

| Key idea | We can take away numbers by splitting them into hundreds, tens and units. |

# MD1.1 Repeated addition

| Key idea | We can write multiplication sentences as addition sentences. |
|---|---|

**A1**

You need 2 dice and counters.
Play with a partner.

Throw one dice. This is the size of the jump.
Throw the other dice to find out how many jumps Fergus makes along the stones.

Write the jumps down as an addition sentence.

Play 10 times each.

**B1** Fergus makes these jumps.

Write them as additions.

$3 \times 4 = 3 + 3 + 3 + 3$

| a | $2 \times 3$ |
| b | $4 \times 5$ |
| c | $6 \times 2$ |

| d | $8 \times 2$ |
| e | $7 \times 3$ |
| f | $5 \times 5$ |

**B2** Where does Fergus land each time in B1?

**C1** You need a 0–100 number line, dice, digit cards 1–9.

Play A1 again.

This time pick a digit card to find the size of a jump.

Use the 0–100 number line to help you find where Fergus lands.

| Key idea | We can write multiplication sentences as addition sentences. |

# MD1.2 Grouping

 **1**   Do A1 with cubes.

Kevin goes back in jumps of the same size and lands exactly on zero.

**A1**   **a**   Start at 8. Find 2 different ways.

| 0 | 1 | 2 | 3 | 4 | 5 | 6 | 7 | 8 |

Write a subtraction and a division sentence for each way.

**b**   Start at 10. Find 2 different ways.

| 0 | 1 | 2 | 3 | 4 | 5 | 6 | 7 | 8 | 9 | 10 |

Write a subtraction and a division sentence for each way.

**B1**   Kevin wants to make equal jumps to get from 12 to 0.
Find as many ways as you can.

| 0 | 1 | 2 | 3 | 4 | 5 | 6 | 7 | 8 | 9 | 10 | 11 | 12 |

Write a subtraction and a division sentence for each way.

**C1**   Do A and B again but this time Kevin jumps in steps of 1.

What do you notice?

| **Key idea** | When we solve a word problem we work out the number sentence needed. |

**A1** The school has 7 rows of 10 chairs.

Tickets
50p each

Interval
Ice cream 20p
Juice 10p

**a** How many chairs altogether?

**b** 12 tickets have been sold. How much money is that?

**c** £2 has been collected from selling programmes. How many have been sold?

**d** In the interval, Helen is going to spend £1.60 on ice creams for her friends. How many can she buy?

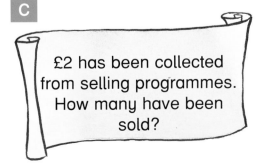

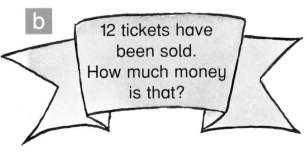

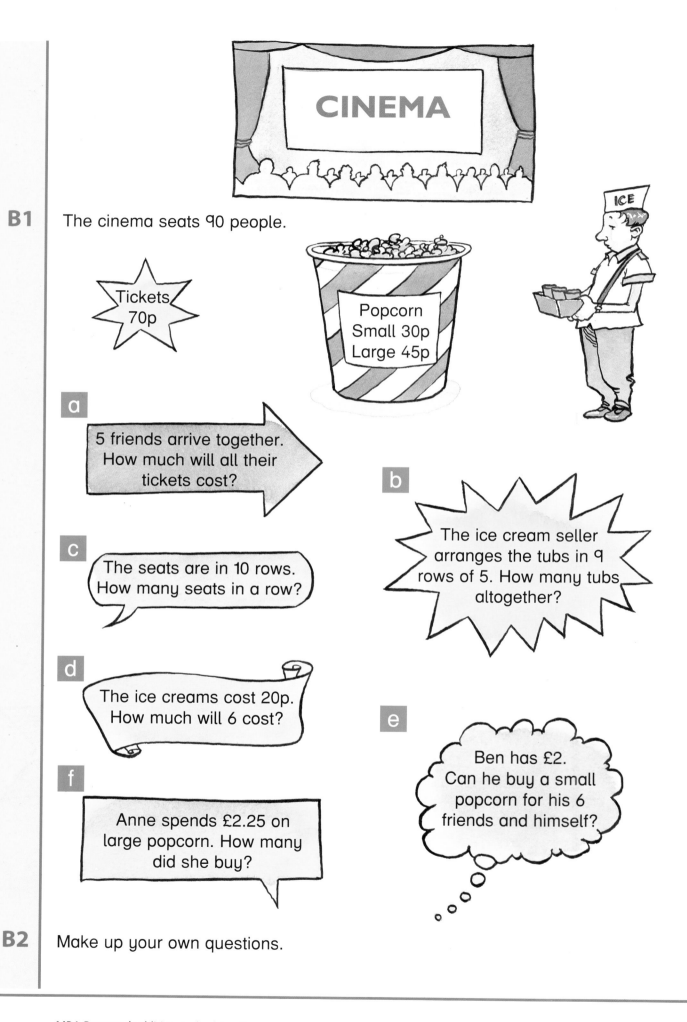

**CINEMA**

**B1** The cinema seats 90 people.

Tickets 70p

Popcorn
Small 30p
Large 45p

**a** 5 friends arrive together. How much will all their tickets cost?

**b** The ice cream seller arranges the tubs in 9 rows of 5. How many tubs altogether?

**c** The seats are in 10 rows. How many seats in a row?

**d** The ice creams cost 20p. How much will 6 cost?

**e** Ben has £2. Can he buy a small popcorn for his 6 friends and himself?

**f** Anne spends £2.25 on large popcorn. How many did she buy?

**B2** Make up your own questions.

MD1 Repeated addition and subtraction

40 chocolate cakes have been cooked.

I have baked 56 loaves of bread.

Special Choc-chip cookies 12p

Special Iced buns only 15p!

**a**
The baker arranges the chocolate cakes in 5 rows. How many in each row?

**b**
Rosa buys 7 iced buns. How much does she spend?

**c**
The bread is put on the shelf in rows of 8. How many rows are there?

**d**
The baker has 3 trays of gingerbread men to sell. How many is that altogether?

**e**
Max spends £1.32 on choc-chip cookies. How many does he buy?

| Key idea | When we solve a word problem we work out the number sentence needed. |
| --- | --- |

# MD2.1 Investigating arrays

| Key idea | We can arrange objects in a rectangular array to find out 'how many'. |
|---|---|

$3 \times 5 = 15$
or $5 \times 3 = 15$

**A1** Write a multiplication fact for each array.

a  ● ● ● ●
   ● ● ● ●

b

c  ▲ ▲ ▲ ▲
   ▲ ▲ ▲ ▲
   ▲ ▲ ▲ ▲
   ▲ ▲ ▲ ▲

d  |||||||||||
   |||||||||||
   |||||||||||

e

f

**A2** Draw and label arrays to show

a $2 \times 5$    b $10 \times 2$    c $5 \times 6$    d $2 \times 7$

**B1** How can you put 12 stamps on a parcel in an array?
Draw them.

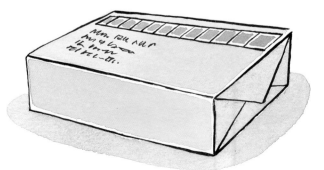

**B2** A board game needs 24 squares.
Draw as many designs as you can.

2s, 5s and 10s

| **Key idea** | We need to know multiplication facts to solve multiplication and division problems. |

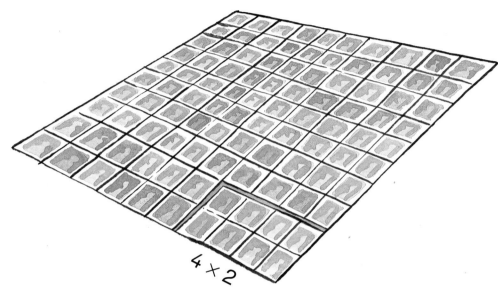

4 × 2

**A1** How many stamps altogether?

a  2 × 10          b  6 × 5          c  6 × 2          d  7 × 5

e  9 × 2           f  5 × 8          g  10 × 10        h  9 × 5

**A2**

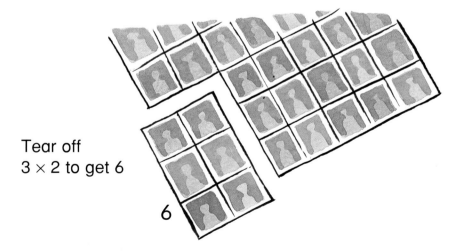

Tear off
3 × 2 to get 6

6

Mrs Smart, the school secretary, needs the following numbers of stamps.
Find a way to tear them off the sheet.

a  18             b  14             c  60             d  25

e  15             f  45             g  90             h  10

**B1**    Mrs Smart says there are different ways to tear off these numbers of stamps.

Try and find them all.

| a | 20 | b | 30 | c | 40 | d | 12 |

**B2**    In the school office, the stamps are kept as:

whole sheets          half sheets          whole strips

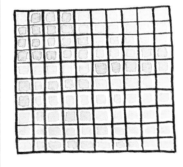 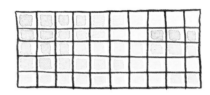 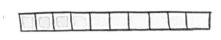

and sheets for tearing.

To make 58 stamps,
use a half sheet and tear off $2 \times 4$.

Make these numbers of stamps.

| a | 15 | b | 34 | c | 75 | d | 160 | e | 178 |

**B3**    Make some totals of your own.

---

| **Key idea** | We need to know multiplication facts to solve multiplication and division problems. |

# Multiplying situations

| **Key idea** | We use multiplication to solve many problems about numbers, objects and measures. |

**A1** A multipack of crisps contains 5 bags. Mum buys 4 multipacks.
How many bags does she buy altogether?

**A2** A chocolate bar costs 10p. How much do 10 bars cost?

**A3** A ball of string is 10 metres long. How long are 2 balls of string?

**A4** It takes me 2 minutes to write a sentence on the computer.
How long does it take me to write 8 sentences?

**A5** One bottle holds 1 litre. How much do 9 bottles hold?

**A6** A mouse weighs 100 grams.
How much do 9 mice weigh?

**A7** A spoon holds 8 millilitres. How much in 10 spoons?

**A8** There are 5 school days in a week.
How many school days are there in half a term (7 weeks)?

MD2 Arrays 2s, 5s, 10s

**B1** 5 cars need 3 new tyres each.
How many new tyres are needed altogether?

**B2** My sister gets £5 pocket money a week.
How much does she get in a month (4 weeks)?

**B3** I collect computer games. Last week 2 of my friends gave me 4 games each.
How many was that?

**B4** 100 grams of sweets cost £1.
How much does 10 times that amount cost?

**B5** I drank 3 glasses of juice on Wednesday and twice that amount on Thursday.
How much did I drink?

**B6** The recipe says to put in 2 teaspoons of water.
One teaspoon holds 5 millilitres. How much water do I put in?

**B7** My sister is 1 metre tall. My dad is double that.
How tall is my dad?

**B8** It takes me 5 minutes to run 1 lap round the park and 10 minutes to walk.
How long do 8 laps take me if I run? How long does this take me to walk?

**C1** Make up some multiplication stories to talk about in the plenary.

| Key idea | We use multiplication to solve many problems about numbers, objects and measures. |

MD2 Arrays 2s, 5s, 10s

# Doubles and halves 1

| **Key idea** | We can use the double and halves we already know to find other doubles and halves quickly. |

Work out these doubles and halves using ones you already know.

'I know double 15 is 30, so I know half 30 is 15'

**A1** Write the double or half that goes with each one.

| a | double 6 | b | double 12 | c | halve 14 |
| d | double 25 | e | halve 26 | f | double 35 |
| g | halve 30 | h | double 50 | i | halve 200 |
| j | double 70 | k | double 150 | l | double 45 |

**B1**

| a | double 200 | b | halve 300 | c | double 18 |
| d | halve 80 | e | double 75 | f | halve 70 |
| g | double 350 | h | halve 800 | i | double 55 |
| j | halve 900 | k | double 85 | l | halve 500 |

**C1**

| a | double 95 | b | halve 170 | c | double 65 |
| d | halve 1000 | e | double 450 | f | halve 34 |

# Doubles and halves 2

| Key idea | We can double and halve in many ways, using +, −, × and ÷ |
|---|---|

★1 Use a number line or cubes or base 10 apparatus.
Write down where the frogs landed.

a I landed on $\frac{1}{2}$ of 6

b I landed on half 20

c I landed on double 7

d I landed on double 9

e I landed on half 16

f I landed on double 4

A1 You need a 0–100 number line.

These frogs each did 2 equal jumps to get from one number to another.
Write a number sentence for each frog.

a I jumped from 18 to 0

b I jumped from 22 to 0

c I jumped from 34 to 0

d I jumped from 0 to 21 to ?

e I jumped from 0 to 24 to ?

f I jumped from 0 to 28 to ?

**B1** You need a number line or other apparatus.

Answer the frog's questions.
Write a number sentence to show your method.

**a** I ate 22 flies on Monday.
On Tuesday I ate double the number.
How many did I eat on Tuesday?

**b** I swam round the pond 25 times.
Now I'm going to swim twice as far.
How many times round the pond is that?

**c** I have 26 friends.
Half are lady frogs.
How many are man frogs?

**d** My friend can leap 45 cm.
I can leap twice as far.
How far is that?

**e** There are 500 litres of water in my pond.
If half dries up, how much is left?

**C1** Find the missing numbers.

**a** $90 + \square = 180$    **b** $\square \div 2 = 43$    **c** $34 \times 2 = \square$

**d** $\frac{1}{2}$ of $250 = \square$    **e** $65 + 65 = \square$    **f** $650 \div 2 = \square$

| Key idea | We can double and halve in many ways, using +, −, × and ÷ |
|---|---|

Making bigger

| Key idea | We can multiply to make things bigger. |
|---|---|

**A1**

Put these things in the machine.
Find out how they come out.
Write a number sentence and the answer.

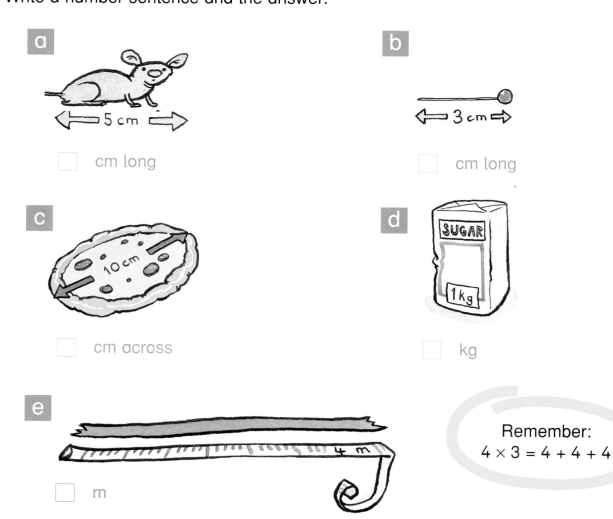

a

5 cm

☐ cm long

b

3 cm

☐ cm long

c

10 cm

☐ cm across

d

SUGAR

1 kg

☐ kg

e

4 m

☐ m

Remember:
$4 \times 3 = 4 + 4 + 4$

**B1**

Draw a machine to make things 4 times bigger.
Put in the things from A1.
Write a number sentence for each one.

Use facts you already
know to help you
multiply by 4.

**C1**

Sam, Kate and Arash like to swim as far as they can.

Arash swims 3 times as far as Kate.

Kate swims 2 times as far as Sam.

**a** One day Sam swims 2 lengths.
How far does Arash swim?
Write a multiplication sentence.

**b** Another day Sam swims 3 lengths.
How far does Arash swim?
Write a multiplication sentence.

**c** Write some more sentences with ×6.

| Key idea | We can multiply to make things bigger. |
|---|---|

3s and 4s

| Key idea | We can use multiplication facts to find all the division facts in any table. |
| --- | --- |

**A1**   Copy and complete the 4 times table.

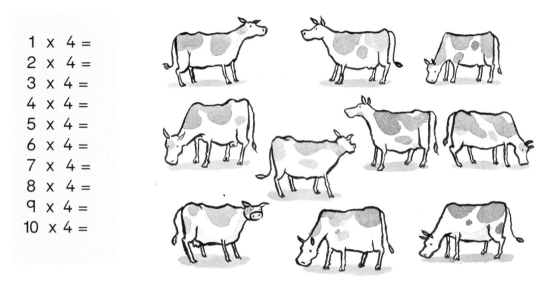

1 x 4 =
2 x 4 =
3 x 4 =
4 x 4 =
5 x 4 =
6 x 4 =
7 x 4 =
8 x 4 =
9 x 4 =
10 x 4 =

**A2**

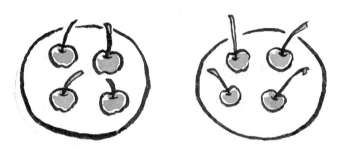

A multiplication question is:

2 plates with 4 cherries each. How many cherries?    $4 \times 2 = 8$

A division question is:

8 cherries, 4 on a plate. How many plates?    $8 \div 4 = 2$

Use the 4 times table to write down division facts.

There are 10 altogether.

**B1** Answer the questions about 3s.

a How many 3s in 21?

b What is 3 times 3?

c What are six 3s?

d What is 8 multiplied by 3?

e Multiply 9 by 3.

f Divide 15 by 3.

**B2** Answer the questions about 4s.

a What are seven 4s?

b What is 6 multiplied by 4?

c How many 4s in 32?

d Divide 20 by 4.

e What is 24 divided by 4?

f How many 4s in 16?

**C1** Use CM 40.

Write as many different questions as you can using the numbers in each star.

This star shows one way to do it.

There are lots of other questions you could ask.

What is 5 times 4?

Multiply 5 by 4.

What is 20 divided by 4?

5   4

20

What are five 4s?

What is 5 multiplied by 4?

Divide 20 by 4.

What is the product of 4 and 5?

How many 4s are in 20?

| Key idea | We can use multiplication facts to find all the divisions facts in any table. |
|---|---|

# MD4.2 Sharing

**B1**

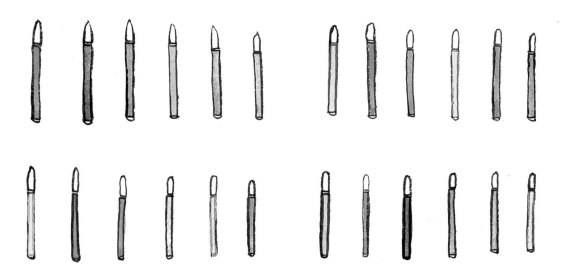

Share 24 pens equally among these numbers of children.

a 1    b 2    c 3    d 4    e 6    f 8    g 12    h 24

How many will each get?

**C1**    Investigate different ways of sharing these numbers of marbles.

a 12    b 20    c 16    d 40

Write down a number sentence for each way.

MD4 Sharing and remainders: 3s and 4s

# Dividing situations

| Key idea | We divide to calculate 'in every' problems because a number has been shared equally. |

The chocolate department is investigating how many chocolates in every layer for each size box.

**Sweet Factory**
**Chocolate box department**

Copy and fill in the △s, ◯s, and ☐s to find how the chocolates could fit.

**A1**  Mini boxes hold 8 chocolates.

$8 \div 8 = \triangle$       $8 \div \triangle = 8$

$8 \div 4 = \triangle$       $8 \div \triangle = 4$

$8 \div 2 = \triangle$       $8 \div \triangle = 2$

$8 \div 1 = \triangle$       $8 \div \triangle = 1$

**A2**  Regular boxes hold 12 chocolates.

$12 \div 2 = \bigcirc$       $12 \div \bigcirc = 2$

$12 \div 3 = \bigcirc$       $12 \div \bigcirc = 3$

$12 \div 4 = \bigcirc$       $12 \div \bigcirc = 4$

$12 \div 6 = \bigcirc$       $12 \div \bigcirc = 6$

**A3**  Large boxes hold 24 chocolates.

$24 \div 8 = \square$       $24 \div \square = 6$

$24 \div 6 = \square$       $24 \div \square = 3$

$24 \div 4 = \square$       $24 \div \square = 8$

$24 \div 3 = \square$       $24 \div \square = 4$

MD4 Sharing and remainders: 3s and 4s

**B1** Look at your chocolate box sentences from A.

This is the large box for 24 ÷ ☐ = 3

Imagine a box for each chocolate box sentence.

**a** Draw the best mini box, the best regular box and best large box.

**b** Explain why you think it is best.

**C1** What numbers of chocolates could the factory use for Family and Giant boxes?

How could they be arranged? ☐ ÷ ☐ = ☐

| **Key idea** | We divide to calculate 'in every' problems because a number has been shared equally. |

# 4.6 Sensible rounding

Do the calculations.
Think about the remainders.
Do they need rounding up or down?

**B1** Motorbikes can carry 2 people safely.
How many motorbikes are needed for 11 people?

**B2** Bus tickets cost £3.
How many tickets can I buy with £20?

**B3** The class is going to play five-a-side football. There are 31 children in the class.
How many teams can they make?

**B4** 2 children can sit at one table. There are 21 children in the class.
How many tables do they need?

**B5** Eggs come in boxes of 6. I need 13 eggs for a giant birthday cake.
How many boxes must I buy?

**B6** 5 people share a prize for £5 million and 1 penny.
How much does each person get?

**B7** I picked 10 kg of strawberries. 1 box holds 3kg.
How many boxes do I need?

**B8** A mini-bus carries 10 people.
How many mini-busses are needed to carry 101 people?

# MD5.1 Using place value to multiply

| Key idea | When we multiply by 10, the units digit moves to be a tens digit and the tens digit moves to be a hundreds digit. |
|---|---|

**A1** Multiply these numbers by 10.
Use the abacus to shift the digits to the left.

a
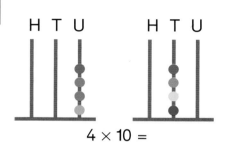
4 × 10 =

b
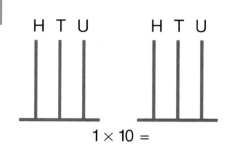
1 × 10 =

c
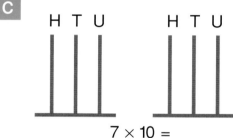
7 × 10 =

d
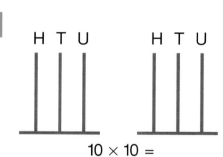
10 × 10 =

**A2** Work in pairs to complete this pattern.
Choose apparatus to help with the third row.

| ↓ | 1 | 2 | 3 | 4 | 5 | 6 | 7 | 8 | 9 | 10 |
|---|---|---|---|---|---|---|---|---|---|---|
| × 10 | 10 | 20 | | | 50 | | | | | |
| × 10 | 100 | | | | 500 | | | | | |

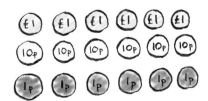
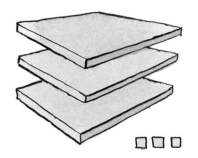
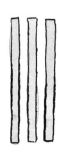

**B1** Use the pattern in A2 to help fill in the missing numbers.

a $5 \times 10 \times 10 = \square$

b $8 \times 10 \times 10 = \square$

c $3 \times 10 \times \square = 300$

d $6 \times \square = 600$

e $\square \times 100 = 200$

f $7 \times \square \times 10 = 700$

**B2** Talk to your partner about a quick way of multiplying by 10.
Explain your answers to B1 to each other.

Be ready for the plenary.

**C1** Multiply these numbers by 10.

a 50    b 14    c 39    d 0    e 100

Write down your answers.
What happens?

Be ready to talk about multiplying 2-digit numbers by 10 in the plenary.

| Key idea | When we multiply by 10, the units digit moves to be a tens digit and the tens digit moves to be a hundreds digit. |
|---|---|

# Using place value to divide

| **Key idea** | When we divide a 'hundreds' number by 10 or 100 the hundreds digit moves to be a tens digit or a units digit. |
| --- | --- |

 **1**  Look what happens when we multiply by 10.

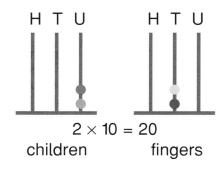

$2 \times 10 = 20$

children        fingers

Copy and write the answers.

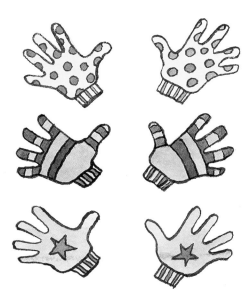

$1 \times 10 =$

$2 \times 10 =$

$3 \times 10 =$

$4 \times 10 =$

$5 \times 10 =$

$6 \times 10 =$

$7 \times 10 =$

$8 \times 10 =$

$9 \times 10 =$

Now do A.

**A1**  Copy these number sentences and fill in the boxes.

**a**  $5 \times 10 = \square$      **b**  $10 \times 8 = \square$

**c**  $4 \times 100 = \square$      **d**  $9 \times 100 = \square$

**e**  $3 \times 1 = \square$      **f**  $\square \times 100 = 200$

**A2**  How many?
Work out using a 'quick' way.

|  | heads | arms | toes |
|---|---|---|---|
| 10 children | | | |
| 100 children | | | |

**A3**  This is the two-headed, three-armed, eight-toed monster.

Work out the number of heads, arms and toes for

**a**  10 monsters,

**b**  100 monsters.

**B1**  Copy these number sentences and fill in the boxes.

**a**  ☐ × 10 = 50     **b**  40 ÷ 10 = ☐

**c**  4 × ☐ = 800     **d**  300 ÷ 100 = ☐

**e**  5 × ☐ = 5     **f**  700 ÷ 10 = ☐

**B2**  The two-headed, three-armed, eight-toed monster invites
9 monster friends to her party.

They eat   40   sandwiches
          300   crisps
          100   chocolate fingers
           20   jellies

How much food does each monster eat?

How much food does each mouth eat?

**C1**  How much does the party cost for each monster?

**Bill**
The jellies cost                    £2.00
The sandwiches cost                 £6.00
The crisps cost                     £3.00
The chocolate fingers cost          £8.00
Fizzy drinks cost                   £5.00

£1 shared
between 10 is 10p.

**C2**  Make up your own party shopping list.
You are allowed to spend the same as the monsters.

| Key idea | When we divide a 'hundreds' number by 10 or 100, the hundreds digit moves to be a tens digit or a units digit. |
|---|---|

Multiples of 10 to 50

| Key idea | $40 \times 30$ is the same as $4 \times 10 \times 3$, or $4 \times 3 \times 10$ |
|---|---|

**A1** Copy the multiplication grid. Fill in the boxes.

| $\times$ | 1 | 2 | 3 | 4 | 5 | 10 |
|---|---|---|---|---|---|---|
| 10 | | | | | | |
| 20 | | | | | | |
| 30 | | | | | | |
| 40 | | | | | | |
| 50 | | | | | | |

**A2** Use IP15.

**a** Bill fetches 4 stacks of breeze blocks.
How many breeze blocks is that?

**b** There are 80 doors in one building.
How many packs of door handles do they need?

**c** Liz needs 50 poles.
How many piles is that?

**d** $\frac{1}{3}$ of the pack of tiles is broken.
How many tiles are broken?

**B1** Copy the number sentences. Fill in the boxes.

    **a** $10 \times 5 = \boxed{\phantom{0}}$     **b** $20 \times 4 = \boxed{\phantom{0}}$     **c** $30 \times \boxed{\phantom{0}} = 90$

    **d** $10 \times \boxed{\phantom{0}} = 500$     **e** $\boxed{\phantom{0}} \times 4 = 100$     **f** $4 \times \boxed{\phantom{0}} = 160$

    **g** $40 = 2 \times \boxed{\phantom{0}}$     **h** $50 = 50 \times \boxed{\phantom{0}}$     **i** $400 = 10 \times \boxed{\phantom{0}}$

**B2** Write down 3 multiplication problems for the building site.
Use multiples of 10.
Ask a friend to solve 1 problem.

**C1** Copy this grid. Work out what goes in the boxes.

| ×  |     | 3   |     |
|----|-----|-----|-----|
| 20 | 40  |     |     |
|    |     | 30  |     |
|    | 100 |     | 250 |

Make up your own grid.

| **Key idea** | $40 \times 30$ is the same as $4 \times 10 \times 3$, or $4 \times 3 \times 10$ |
|---|---|

# Linking multiplication and division statements

| Key idea | We can make up to 3 more sentences from 1 multiplication fact. |

$$3 \times 2 = 6$$

$$2 \times 3 = 6$$

$$6 \div 3 = 2$$

$$6 \div 2 = 3$$

**A1** Write 4 facts from each array.

a

b

**A2** Copy and complete.

a  $5 \times 3 = \square$

$3 \times 5 = \square$

$15 \div 3 = \square$

$15 \div 5 = \square$

b  $6 \times 3 = \square$

$3 \times 6 = \square$

$18 \div 3 = \square$

$18 \div 6 = \square$

**A3** Write out 4 facts for each trio.

a  | 5 | 2 | 10 |

b  | 7 | 5 | 35 |

**B1** a Write out 2 facts for this trio.  | 5 | 5 | 25 |

b Explain why there are only 2 facts.

c Find other trios where 2 numbers are the same.

**B2** Find some trios with two 2-digit numbers, and one 1-digit number.
Write the linked facts. Write a number story for your trio.

# MD6.5 Using inverse operations

**Key idea** | We can check any calculation by undoing it or doing it in a different way.

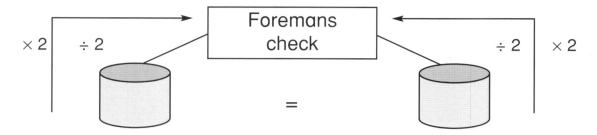

**A1** Which calculations could the foreman use to check which?
Match the calculation to the foreman's check.

| Calculation | Check |
|---|---|
| 30 x 2 = 60 | 60 ÷ 2 = 30 |
| Half of 60 is 30 | 60 ÷ 30 = 2 |
| 2 x 30 = 60 | Double 30 is 60 |

**A2** Show how the foreman could check these calculations.

a  Half of 60 is 30

b  Half of 80 is 40

c  10 ÷ 2 = 5

d  100 ÷ 2 = 50

e  Double 50 is 100

f  Double 54 is 108

g  20 × 2 = 40

h  55 × 2 = 110

**A3** Copy and complete.

The opposite of multiplication is _____.

The opposite of division is _____.

The opposite of doubling is _____.

The opposite of halving is _____.

division

halving

multiplication

doubling

**A4** Make up your own building problems using × and ÷
Calculate. Ask your partner to check them.

MD6 Multiplying by 2, 3, 4 or 5

$30 \times 2 + 5 \times 2 = 70$     $70 \div 2 = 35$

**B1** How could the foreman find and check the following numbers of planks.

**a** $54 \div 2$

**b** $32 \times 2$

**c** $60 \times 10$

**d** $92 \div 2$

**e** Half of 120

**f** Double 71

**g** A third of 33

**h** A quarter of 88

**B2**

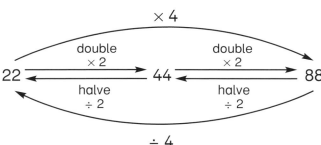

Use doubling and halving twice to check these.

**a** $52 \times 4 = 208$

**b** $31 \times 4 = 124$

**c** $84 \div 4 = 21$

**d** $168 \div 4 = 42$

**B3** Has the foreman got these calculations right?
Check using an equivalent calculation.

**a** $60 \div 3 = 20$

**b** $31 \times 5 = 150$

**c** $55 \div 5 = 11$

**d** $43 \times 3 = 126$

| Key idea | We can check any calculation by 'undoing it' or doing it in a different way. |
|---|---|

# SP1.1 Solving puzzles

| Key idea | We can explain how we solved a puzzle and why we did it that way. |
|---|---|

**1** Use cubes to do A.

**A1** What if one domino in each pair is blank?

Find all the pairs of dominoes with a total of 8 spots.

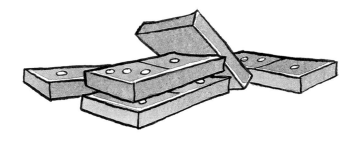

**B1** What if one domino in each pair has zero in one half?

Find all the pairs of dominoes with a total of 8 spots.

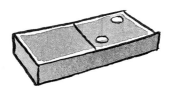

**B2** Find as many other pairs of dominoes with a total of 8 spots as you can.

**C1** Find as many other pairs of dominoes with a total of 10 spots as you can.

CM 55

Simple story problems

| Key idea | We can choose how to solve a word problem. |

**A1** A ladybird has 6 legs.

a How many legs do 4 ladybirds have?

b How many legs do 6 ladybirds have?

**A2** There are 24 chocolates in a box.

a How many people can eat 3 chocolates each?

b How many chocolates are left if you eat 18?

c How many chocolates are there in 2 boxes?

d How many boxes are needed to hold 72 chocolates?

**B1** Make up stories to go with these number sentences.

a  15 + 4 = 19     b  38 − 12 = 26     c  76 − 28 = 48

**B2** Liam thinks of a number, doubles it and adds 4.

The answer is 20.

What was his number?

**B3** There are 16 books on the bottom shelf and 39 books on the top shelf.

Carol takes 26 of the books away.

How many books are left?

**C1** Make up 3 number puzzles for someone to solve.

| Key idea | We can choose how to solve a word problem. |

| Key idea | Explaining a word problem helps us to solve it. |
|---|---|

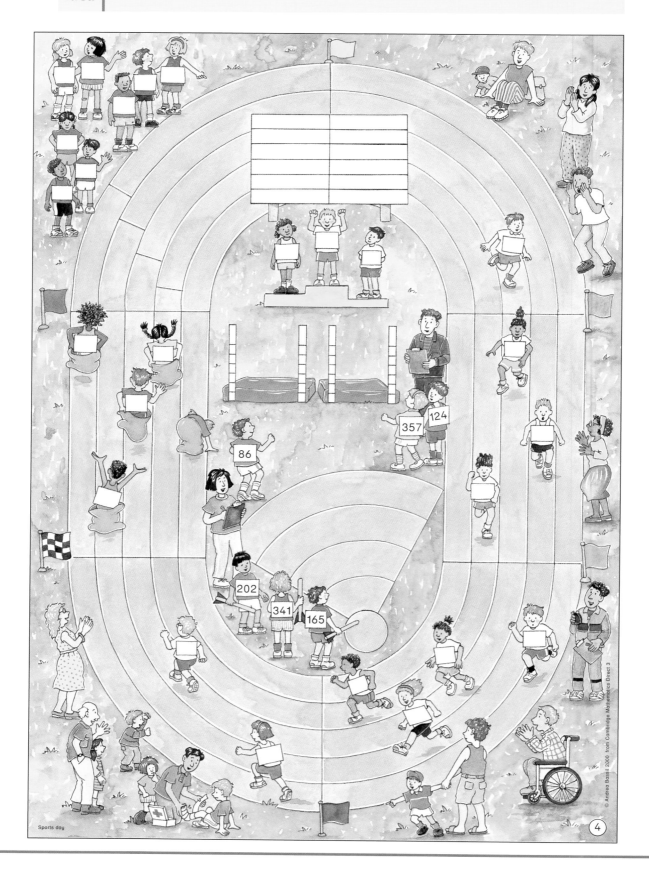

Sports day

| Key idea | We can use +, −, × or ÷ to solve problems. |
|---|---|

**A1** Use the menu from 'The Caveman's Café'.

Order a drink and something to eat for you and your friends.

How much do you each pay?

• MENU •

| Worm mousse | £1.25 |
|---|---|
| Turtle eggs | £1.75 |
| Varanosaurus stew | £4.20 |
| Coco-nut-ola | £1.10 |
| Mammoth burger | £3.99 |
| Crispy fins | £1.80 |
| Pineapple fizz | £1.20 |
| Berry shake | £0.85 |

**A2** How much change from £5 for

a  Varanosaurus stew?

b  Mammoth burger?

c  Coco-nut-ola?

d  Berry shake?

**B1** | **Which operation?**

Write a number sentence with +, −, ×, or ÷ for each problem.

a | 4 woolly mammoths. How many legs?

b | 1 pineapple fizz and 1 burger. How much?

c | 16 people and 4 tables. How many people at each table?

d | 6 waiters. 2 in the kitchen. How many staff in the café?

**B2** | Make up your own word problem for each operation.

Write a number sentence each time.

**C1** | Order some meals for £3 or less.

a | Write a bill for each one.

b | How many of each meal can you order for less than £30?

Investigate.

| **Key idea** | We can use +, −, × or ÷ to solve problems. |

# Using + and − to solve problems

| **Key idea** | We can use + and − to solve word problems. |
| --- | --- |

Alicia and Jon collect stamps.

**A1** Alicia has collected 18 French and 17 Spanish stamps.
How many on this double page?

**A2** Jon has collected 35 Australian and 40 New Zealand stamps.
How many on this double page?

**A3** Jon had 46 Portuguese stamps.
He gives half of them to Alicia.
How many do they each have?

**A4** Alicia has 72 Indian stamps and gives 30 to Jon in return.
How many Indian stamps has she got left?

**A5**  Alicia's aunt sent her 47 stamps from Canada. She already had 24.
How many does she have now?

**A6**  Jon had 73 British stamps. 28 were 1st class.
How many other British stamps did he have?

**B1**  Alicia has 34 Polish stamps and 19 German stamps.

Jon has 27 on his double page.
How many more does Alicia have?

**B2**  Jon had 64 Greek stamps. He swaps half of them with Alicia.
He gives half of what is left away.
How many does he have left?

**C1**  Make up 3 'stamp' problems of your own.

| **Key idea** | We can use + and − to solve word problems. |
| --- | --- |

Choosing which way to add

| Key idea | Sometimes pencil and paper methods are helpful when we solve an addition problem. |
|---|---|

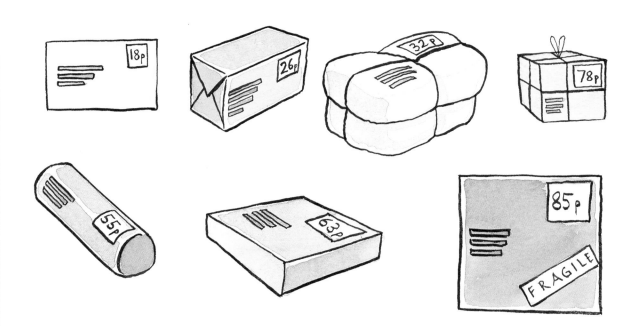

**A1** I want to send all of these packages but I only have £1.40.
I decide to send 2 today, and the rest when I've been to the bank.

a Find a pair of packages I can send today.

b Find a pair of packages I can't send today.

c What are the most expensive packages I could send today?

d Find 3 other pairs of packages I can send today.
How much does each pair cost to send?

**B1** Can I send 3 or more packages?
Find all the sets of 3 packages I can send with my £1.40.

**C1** What if I had £1.50? Find all the sets of packages I could send.

# SP3.3 Missing numbers

Write a number sentence to solve each problem.

**A1** There are 4 panes of glass in each window.

**a** How many panes are in 5 windows?

**b** How many panes in 50 windows?

**A2** A building needs 35 doors.
Another building needs 44 doors.
How many doors altogether?

**A3** Bill ordered 29 bags of cement.
15 have been used.
How many left?

**A4** To lay the bricks for 1 wall, Bill needs to mix:

50 kg cement

200 kg sand

25 l water

How much cement, sand and water does he need for

**a** 2 walls?          **b** 4 walls?

**B1** Jo needs 3 more floorboards, each 50 cm long.
She cuts them from a plank of wood 2 m 20 cm long.
How long is the wood that is left?

**B2** There are 6 floorboards in a stack.
Jo uses 4 stacks to lay the floor in 1 room.

**a** How many boards has she used?

**b** How many of the same floors can she lay with 28 stacks?

**B3** Make up some building story problems for these number sentences.

**a** 24 + ☐ = 39

**b** 4 × 8 = ☐

**C1** There are 88 bricks in a stack.

Liz is building a wall.
She can carry 12 bricks up the ladder each time.

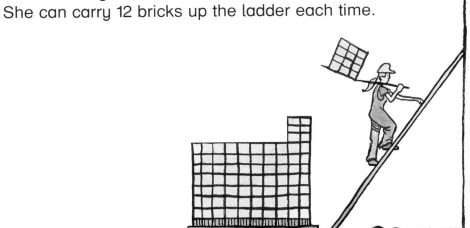

**a** Investigate how many times she has to go up the ladder.
Explain how you solved the problem.

**b** What if she can only carry 11 bricks each time?

**c** What if . . . .?

| **Key idea** | We can write a number sentence with a missing number to help us solve a problem. |
|---|---|

# SP3.4

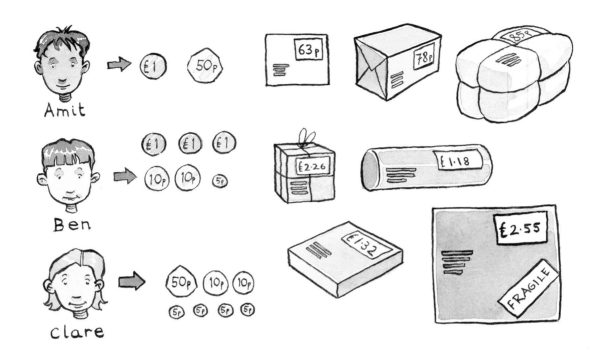

Solve these problems.
Decide which sort of calculation to use to get the right answer quickly.
Show what you did by recording your working as a number sentence.

**A1** How much money have the children got altogether?

**A2**  **a** Who has the most money?  **b** Who has the least money?

**c** What is the difference between the most and the least amounts?

**A3**  **a** How many 25p stamps can Amit buy?

**b** How much money would he have left?

**A4** Choose a package that Clare could afford to post.

**a** With which coins might she pay?

**b** How much change would she get?

**A5**

**a** Find a package that Amit cannot afford to post.

**b** How much more money does he need in order to post this package?

**B1**

**a** Next week Amit will have twice as much money as he has now.
How much will he have?

**b** Clare will have three times as much as she has now.
How much will she have?

**c** Who will have the most money next week?

**d** How many 25p stamps can Clare buy next week?

**B2** Ben and Clare put their money together to send 3 parcels.

**a** Which 3 parcels might they send?

**b** How much money will they have left?

| **Key idea** | We can use +, −, ×, ÷ to solve money problems. |
| --- | --- |

Solving 2-step problems

| Key idea | Find an approxiamate answer before solving a problem; check the answer afterwards. |

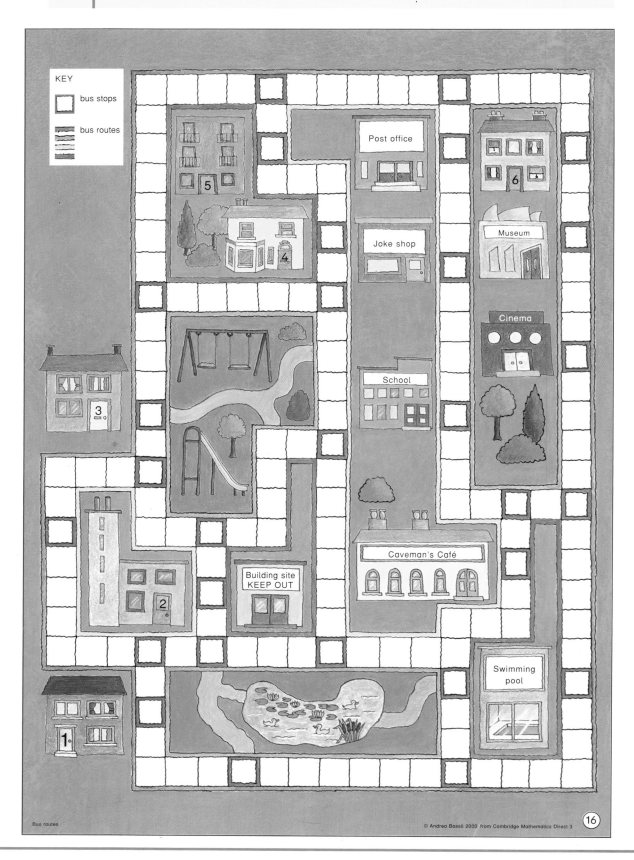

KEY

☐ bus stops

☰ bus routes

5

4

Post office

Joke shop

6

Museum

Cinema

3

School

2

Building site KEEP OUT

Caveman's Café

1

Swimming pool

Bus routes

© Andrea Bossil 2000 from Cambridge Mathematics Direct 3

16